The Fatfield Recipe Book

The
FATFIELD
Recipe Book
MEGA MEALS · MINI CALORIES

Sally Ann Voak

Michael O'Mara Books Limited

First published in 1992 by
Michael O'Mara Books Limited,
9 Lion Yard, Tremadoc Road, London SW4 7NQ

A CIP catalogue record for this book is available
from the British Library

ISBN 1-85479-121-4

Designed by Mick Keates
Edited by Fiona Holman

Typeset by Florencetype Ltd, Kewstoke, Avon
Printed and bound by Cox & Wyman, Reading

Acknowledgements

Many thanks to all the Fatfield slimmers who
tried out my recipes (and lived!), my assistant
Toni Tompsett, and our home economist
Glynis McGuinness who checked my
calculations so patiently.

CONTENTS

CHOOSING A DIET

All the recipes can be used with the eating programmes from my previous book, *The Fatfield Diet*. Alternatively, you can use them with the diets in Chapter Two of this book (page 13). Don't forget to vary your meal choices as much as possible so you get plenty of vitamins and minerals. Where a recipe is very low in calories, do add fresh fruit or bread to bump up the total.

As a guide, a piece of fresh fruit (apple, orange, pear, small banana, two plums, a couple of satsumas) contains about 50 calories, and a medium-thick slice of wholemeal bread from a large cut loaf contains about 70 calories. If there is a recipe which you would love to choose but is rather high in calories, you can always leave out your daily treat – but please don't do that too often as treats give you a valuable psychological boost!

Here's a list of the 10 eating programmes explained in *The Fatfield Diet*, with a guide to which recipes to choose:

● *Basic Fatfield Plan* (*The Fatfield Diet*, page 43). You can choose any breakfast that's 250 calories or under. Lunches should be 350 calories and suppers around 400.
● *Quick Weight Loss Plan* (*The Fatfield Diet*, page 48). This plan is lower in calories, allowing about 1000 daily. So, you should choose 200 calorie breakfasts, 300 calorie lunches, and 350 calorie suppers.
● *Steady Weight Loss Plan* (*The Fatfield Diet*, page 51). Breakfasts are 250 calories, lunches are 350 calories, and suppers go up to 400 calories.
● *Anti-Bloating Plan* (*The Fatfield Diet*, page 55). Breakfasts allow 200 calories, lunches 300, and suppers 350. Choose recipes which include citrus fruits (oranges,

lemons), and green vegetables. Cut down on salty foods like bacon, canned soups and nuts.

• *Heavy-Duty Plan* (*The Fatfield Diet*, page 58). This diet is for men in heavy, outdoor work, so the calorie allowance is about 1800. You can choose breakfasts up to 300 calories, lunches up to 450 calories, and suppers up to 500 calories.

• *Boozers' Plan* (*The Fatfield Diet*, page 61). You are given a generous booze allowance on this plan, so limit breakfasts to 250 calories, lunches to 350 calories, and suppers to 400 calories.

• *Lazy Cooks' Plan* (*The Fatfield Diet*, page 65). The recipes in this book are all fairly simple, but you can choose the easiest ones of all for your diet. Allow yourself 250 calories for breakfast, 300 for lunch, and 400 for supper.

• *Vegetarian Plan* (*The Fatfield Diet*, page 67). There are plenty of choices for you in Chapter Nine of this book, Veggie Slimsations (page 121). Stick to these calorie-counts: breakfast, 300, lunch 350, supper 400.

• *Shift-Workers Plan* (*The Fatfield Diet*, page 71). Chapter Four of this book, Packed Lunches, Snacks and Naughty Nibbles (page 43) will be specially useful for you. But do invest in a wide-topped vacuum flask so you can transport some of the hot dishes to work. Your diet is fully calorie-counted, so it will be easy for you to pick out menus from the wide selection of recipes in this book.

• *Maintenance Plan* (*The Fatfield Diet*, page 120). Adapt this diet to suit yourself, adding calories (about 100 a day) until you achieve the level that suits you. Start with around 1500 calories (1800 for men), working up to a maximum of 2000 (women), 2500 (men in sedentary jobs) or 2800 (men in heavy-duty jobs).

USING THE RECIPES

Every recipe in this book is simple to prepare.

● First, read through the ingredients and step-by-step preparation and cooking methods. Next, check your storecupboard, fridge or freezer for ingredients already available.

● When shopping, take the book with you, so you have a handy list in your basket.

● Work through each step carefully, and you are guaranteed success.

Recipe Notes

● Measurements are given both in imperial and metric amounts, but follow one set of measurements only.

● All spoon measures are level. If you use heaped spoonfuls remember the calorie counts will alter! One tablespoon (tbsp) = 15ml, one dessertspoon (dsp) = 10ml and one teaspoon (tsp) = 5ml.

● Ovens should always be preheated to the specified temperature.

● Eggs are size 3 or medium unless the recipe says otherwise.

● Use freshly ground black pepper when the recipe calls for pepper.

CHAPTER ONE

THE PROOF
OF THE PUDDING

Once upon a time, there was a whole village full of people who loved their food and drink but worried about their weight problems. A year later, they were eating and drinking more than ever before – but had *lost* over half a *ton* of wobbles between them!

Sounds like a fairytale? It's *true*. The village in question is Fatfield, Tyne and Wear, England, and the 50-strong slimming group which meets there every week in the local pub is the pride of the North East. They are living proof that losing weight doesn't have to be a miserable slog, or some kind of penance. Instead, it can be fun, and you really *can* eat more and weigh less.

The Fatfield slimming experiment was started in January 1990 for the BBC-1 magazine programme, 'Bazaar'. As Slimming Editor of *The Sun* newspaper, I had previously supervised large-scale weight-shedding projects with the village of Broadbottom, near Manchester, and Tommyfields Market in Oldham, Lancashire. So, when the producer of 'Bazaar', Erica Griffiths, asked me to organize a similar experiment in Fatfield, I wasn't at all daunted even though the success (or otherwise!) of the slim-in would be followed by millions of TV viewers as well as our 12-million-strong army of *Sun* readers. Indeed, I welcomed the chance to prove that you can tuck into huge platefuls of food at every meal, enjoy meals out, and even drink alcohol while you slim.

At first, our slimmers couldn't believe that they would lose weight so painlessly, and feel so good. But, as the weeks passed they became convinced that the Fatfield Diet isn't just a slimming programme, it's a way of life. They took up all kinds of fitness activities, from horse-riding to aquarobics. They also started working out their own recipes and meal plans, following the rules laid down in the Fatfield Diet.

The first 50 Fatfield slimmers have now expanded to hundreds of thousands – thanks to 'Bazaar', *The Sun*, and the first book about the experiment, *The Fatfield Diet*. Our fame is spreading . . . but our fans are shrinking!

Here are some comments from Fatfield slimmers. Mrs Dawn Toft from Willenhall, West Midlands, wrote: 'I started my Fatfield Diet on 24th June 1991 weighing 10 stone 8lb (67kg), and after eight weeks my weight has reduced to 9 stone 10lb (61kg).' Mrs S. Taylor from Truro, Cornwall wrote: 'Thank you for writing a good diet book at last. I started last week, and never ate so much. I've tried so many diets, but this is the best yet.' Diane Griffiths from Quedgeley, Gloucester, says: 'I have been on your diet for two weeks, by which time I usually start thinking about giving up, but I really enjoy this diet.' Bill Ord, from Washington, Tyne and Wear, said: 'I have lost over a stone, and now enjoy a much more active life – thank you.'

This, second, book is a direct result of our months of work with the Fatfield villagers. It is the most useful recipe book ever written for slimmers because all the ideas have been suggested, tried and tested by 'real' people, not just cookery 'experts' who have never had to queue at a supermarket checkout or budget for a family of four on a small, fixed income. Women with jobs and families to look after, men who love traditional grub like roast Sunday dinners and bangers and mash, couples who want to eat well, but have to stick to a budget – we have consulted people like these every step of the way.

The recipes are easy and practical and include the kinds of foods that we all dish up for our families, as well as special occasion menus. There are plenty of recipes for the growing number of vegetarians, plus Continental dishes and easy microwave ideas. The difference? In each recipe, the calories have been pared down to rock bottom without sacrificing taste or bulk. This has been done by trimming back on sugar-loaded and high-fat items like cream, butter, margarine and cooking oil, and increasing high-fibre ingredients such as fruit, beans, peas, potatoes and bread.

But sweet-tooth slimmers have been catered for too, with a selection of unbelievably low-calorie desserts in Chapter Ten.

The recipes can be used by any weight and health-conscious cook, but they are obviously particularly useful for anyone wishing to slim the Fatfield way. Below, are the rules to follow if you want to win that slimming battle once and for all!

THE FATFIELD DIET RULES

1. Forget any other diet you have tried and stop feeling guilty about your so-called 'failure'. Start afresh with this plan, and think positive. You can do it. (There are 10, practical plans in the first book, *The Fatfield Diet*, and three more variations in Chapter Two of this book.)

2. Consult your doctor before you start. This is always a good idea, and essential if you have a lot of weight to lose, are suffering from ill-health or taking medication of any kind. Show your doctor the recipes and menus.

3. Eat at least three large meals every day. When you look at the diets on pages 14–34, you will see that you are sometimes allowed even more than three meals, plus a daily 'treat'. Eat every scrap and enjoy it. You will lose weight permanently if you never go hungry. Cutting out meals is the quickest way to a life-long weight problem.

4. Pile 'free' vegetables (see the list on page 7) onto your plate. It is a good idea to serve up your meals on a 'Fatfield' platter. A typical Fatfield plate measures 18in (46cm) across and can hold a lot of food. You may have something similar in your crockery cupboard which you currently use as a vegetable plate. Use it for your own meals, piled high with vegetables and salad.

5. Enjoy every mouthful. Eat slowly, chewing your food thoroughly. Sit at a table, or relax at your office desk. Don't eat while you are watching TV, listening to the radio or talking on the telephone.

6. Keep a food 'diary'. Every day, write down everything you eat and drink, where you were, who you were with, and how you felt at the time. At the end of the week, go through it carefully and check it against your diet plan. You'll be able to pinpoint problem areas, and this will help you to tackle them.

7. Write and let me know how you get on! Yes, I really do want to hear from you. Send me 'before' and 'after' pictures if you like, and full details. The address is: Sally Ann Voak, PO Box 618, Coulsdon, Surrey, CR5 1RU.

TEN REASONS WHY IT WORKS

1. It cuts back on FAT. Fat in food provides about 40 per cent of our daily calories. It can be the obvious kind of fat (in fry-ups, takeaways or dairy products like milk and cheese) or the hidden kind (in sausages, made-up meats or pastries). In the Fatfield Diet, fat is cut right down without sacrificing taste, and you can still eat sausages, chips and cheese (the low-fat kind!).

2. You eat less sugar. Sugar is just 'empty' calories and, again, it crops up 'hidden' in foods like fizzy drinks, puddings and even savoury dishes.

3. There's no calorie counting. All the calculations are done for you, so you simply choose the meals you fancy from the lists given.

4. You get plenty of choice. In my experience, slimmers are more likely to stick to an eating programme, long-term, if the menus are varied. It is also much healthier to eat a variety of foods than to stick to a faddish diet with no choices.

5. You never feel hungry. Fibre, nutrition's 'incredible bulk' is the stuff that helps make meals more filling. It is the skeleton of the plant, giving it structure and form. It is also good for you, helping to prevent such nasties as constipation and even cancer of the colon. The best sources of fibre are things like fresh fruit and vegetables (particularly baked potatoes), wholemeal bread and whole grains. The Fatfield Diet contains plenty of it!

6. It fits in with every lifestyle. Whether you are a shiftworker, hold down a nine-to-five job, or are at home, the Fatfield Diet can work for you. The foods are reasonably priced, and available everywhere. The rest of the family will enjoy them too.

7. You can see results – immediately. The diet works from Day One. Obviously, your weight-loss will depend on your starting weight, genetic make-up, metabolism and lifestyle, but you will certainly lose! Sorry, but there is no hard scientific evidence that you will lose it quicker from one part of your body than another. However, women do tend to build up more fat around their hips, thighs and bottoms and men get fat around their tummies – so, those are the most likely shrinking spots.

8. You don't have to give up the treats you love. You can have a certain amount of alcohol, and some sweet treats on the diet. You never feel deprived.

9. The weight will stay off. You eat so much on the diet, that you will *not* feel like pigging out as soon as you reach your target weight.

10. It's fun. Eating good food is one of life's top pleasures, and the diet lets you indulge to your heart's content. No wonder it has been so successful for so many people.

FREE VEGETABLE LIST

Certain vegetables are so low in calories that you can eat them freely on the Fatfield Diet. Serve them lightly boiled, steamed or as huge salads. Never add butter or oil. Instead, sprinkle vegetable dishes with chopped parsley or add wedges of lemon to dishes of green beans or broccoli. Use one of the Fatfield Dressings (*see* recipes, page 53) on salads, or just make up your own with crushed garlic (optional), herbs, lemon juice and vinegar. Wine vinegar or one of the herb-flavoured varieties that you can now buy at supermarkets make the dressing more exciting than malt vinegar.

Where possible, shop for fresh vegetables. Check out the local markets (Friday at around 4.30pm is a great time for bargains in most street markets), or farms. Keep a good selection of frozen vegetables in your freezer or the freezer section of your fridge.

Here's the list of 'free' vegetables:

Asparagus	Fennel
Beansprouts	Gherkins
Broccoli	Leeks
Cabbage	Lettuce
Cauliflower	Mushrooms
Celeriac	Mustard and Cress
Celery	Peppers (red and green)
Chicory	Radishes
Chinese Leaves	Runner Beans
Chives	Shallots
Courgettes	Spinach
Cucumber	Spring Onions (scallions)
Curly Kale	Tomatoes (canned or fresh)
Endive	Watercress

NEW WAYS TO SERVE VEGETABLES

1. Try a Fatfield 'stir-fry'. Chop a selection of vegetables finely. Add a small can of chopped tomatoes to a non-stick pan (you don't need fat), and then the rest of the vegetables. Cook gently until tender but still crunchy, season and flavour with herbs and lemon juice. You can eat as much as you like!

2. Make imaginative salads. There are lots of ideas in this book, but you can also work out your own by experimenting. Do try using vegetables like leaf spinach, fennel (partly cooked), canned asparagus, raw cauliflower and finely sliced leeks.

3. Enjoy 'veggie' casseroles. You can make a superb casserole by layering vegetables in a deep, ovenproof dish, pouring on stock and cooking gently in the oven. Eat it freely on the diet.

4. Keep a dish of vegetables in the fridge. Choose a selection of raw veggies for nibbles, or a casserole (see above) which is delicious eaten cold, too. It is comforting to know that there is always something available to eat between meals even though, on this diet, people rarely seem to need it!

WHY IT'S GREAT TO BE GREEDY

The main reason that the Fatfield Diet works so well is that slimmers can eat PILES of food, and still lose weight. At no time do you feel hungry or deprived; in fact, I have had 'complaints' from some slimmers about the amount of food they are allowed to eat. This is because many over-weight people become used to neglecting 'set' meals in favour of less satisfying but more fattening snacks.

For instance, one Fatfield slimmer told me that, before buying the first book, she hadn't eaten a proper meal, apart from the occasional takeaway, for more than a year. She was existing on biscuits, sandwiches and the rest of the family's leftovers. Despite this, an analysis of her actual food and drink consumption (including things like the double cream she licked off the inside of a foil lid, and the pints of orange juice she drank to keep her 'healthy') showed that her daily calorie intake was 3000. Consequently, although the prospect of sitting down to a proper meal proved to be quite daunting, she was delighted when she found that she could cut her daily calorie intake to 1500 and feel full up all the time.

Linda Philpott, a glamorous grandmother who is one of our Fatfield village slimmers has lost 2 stone (13kg) on the diet. She says: 'Before I started the Fatfield Diet, I kidded myself that it would be better for my figure to nibble little snacks than eat a lot at mealtimes. My family couldn't understand why I didn't lose weight because they never saw me eat anything. When I suddenly started piling my plate with vegetables at suppertime, no-one believed I would be successful. I had doubts myself, until the scales proved me wrong!' Linda now actually enjoys cooking meals the Fatfield way (her recipe is on page 127), and her family have got used to seeing her tuck into delicious, filling dishes.

Before you try the recipes, check through your kitchen utensils and equipment. It could be that you are consuming more calories than you need to because your pans are so old that you pour in loads of oil to stop food burning. Maybe you don't possess really attractive oven-to-tableware. Perhaps your knives are so blunt that you hack off big chunks of food instead of slicing things neatly.

Ask your family to buy you some new equipment as a treat. Personally, I love getting kitchen equipment for birthday presents, especially if there's some frilly under-wear hidden inside the casserole or saucepan!

There are also some basic cooking methods you should learn. You may find that they contradict many of the things you were taught at school or by your mum. However, I can assure you that they will save you MEGA amounts of calories, and actually help improve the taste of food.

EQUIPMENT CHECK-LIST

1. Invest in non-stick pans. A large, shallow one (prob-ably called a frying pan, but you won't be using it for frying!), can do double duty as a 'wok', and for cooking fish, meat and vegetables. Deep saucepans in different sizes are great for sauces, vegetables, stews and pasta.

2. Be a casserole lover. I adore the earthenware oven-to-table type because they look so homely when I put them on the supper table. There are also some very pretty floral and plain oval or round casseroles available which are easier to keep clean than the clear toughened glass type. It's useful to have three sizes – small for individual portions, then a $1^{1}/_{2}$ – 2pt (900ml–1.2 litre) size, and a 3pt (1.8 litre) size for larger amounts. My own favourite is a huge, round French casserole dish which only just fits into my oven. I use it for large amounts of the Coq-Au-Vin (page 94), and the Beef Stew with Newcastle Brown Ale (page 59), which I serve up for buffet parties. It also does double duty as a punch-bowl.

3. Sharpen up your knife drawer. Blunt knives are more dangerous than sharp ones because you hack away with them, instead of cutting cleanly. I find that my small knife with a serrated edge is most useful for slicing tomatoes, cucumber and celery. You also need a good meat knife, a bread knife, and a sharp potato peeler. Don't forget wooden spoons and special spatulas for stirring food in non-stick pans.

4. Buy a blender. Although you can always mash or strain food to produce a purée, a blender is more efficient and fun to use. I have never owned a food processor (because I enjoy chopping vegetables and herbs using a good old chopping board and knife and burn off calories while I'm doing it!), but I wouldn't be without my blender. It's great for low-calorie soups and sauces, dressings and healthy drinks.

5. Weigh up the value of kitchen scales. I think the scales you use in the kitchen are *more* useful than the ones you keep in the bathroom! You need them for successful cooking, and to keep those portion sizes under control. On the Fatfield Diet, you are allowed a lot of 'free' foods, but certain calorie-intensive things like meat, cheese, and nuts must be weighed, otherwise you'll consume more than you think. Choose a brand which is sensitive to within ¼oz (7g).

6. The following are some extras worth having. Although a microwave oven certainly isn't essential, it is very useful indeed for slimmers because it cooks with moist heat and there is no need to use butter or oil to prevent food from sticking. It also preserves important vitamins and minerals. Another luxury which is useful if you can afford one is a slow cooker. It helps save cash because food is cooked slowly at a low temperature, and you can use cheaper cuts of meat. But make sure you still select lean cuts, and skim off fat before serving. A steamer is also a good buy for cooking vegetables *al dente*, nice and crunchy with the goodness intact!

COOKING METHODS

As you read through the recipes in this book, you'll find that certain cooking techniques are used again and again. This is because they ensure maximum flavour and goodness while adding few, or even *no* calories during cooking. In some recipes, we have changed the traditional cooking method in order to reduce calories.

Here's a list of the methods used:

Baking This is great for cooking casseroles, and vegetables such as potatoes. You don't need to add fat.

Dry-frying If you want to seal in the flavour of meat, you can do it by searing it quickly in a non-stick pan. Again, there is no need to add extra fat. When you dry-fry minced beef, you will see that a lot of fat runs out, even from the leanest kind. This can be discarded before adding the rest of the ingredients. To get rid of even more fat, it's a good idea to put the meat onto a sheet of absorbent kitchen paper after dry-frying.

Grilling Always place food on a rack in a baking dish or grill-pan, so that any fat drops through and can be discarded. Grilling is also useful for browning the top of a casserole dish or toasted snack. Many cookers have small second ovens which have a built-in grill. These are extremely useful for baking delicious vegetable or meat dishes which require last-minute browning.

Poaching You need just a little water to poach fish, chicken breast or vegetables like mushrooms and finely chopped onions. This adds NO calories to the food. As a good example of the value of poaching, the calorie content of 4oz (100g) sliced fried button mushrooms is 200. Poached in a little water or stock, the mushrooms contain only 15 calories! I sometimes use canned chopped tomatoes as a poaching liquid, adding finely shredded chicken or flaked fish plus chopped onion to make a sauce for pasta.

Roasting If you usually baste meat during roasting, try cooking it on a rack, and using stock or broth for basting instead of the grease in the pan. After cooking, pop the pan in the fridge so the fat on top hardens. Then, you can quickly skim it off, leaving the nutrient-rich stock which is useful for gravy or soup.

Stir-frying It's possible to cook most stir-fries without adding oil. If you add a little water or stock to the pan to prevent burning, then toss in the pieces of meat, fish or vegetables, you'll find that the food cooks very well indeed.

CHAPTER TWO

EAT MORE, WEIGH LESS

If you slim the Fatfield way, your life will never be the same again! Don't worry, it will change for the better! You'll lose weight, and experience all the benefits of good nutrition, from increased energy to a definite improvement in your health. If you have always gone down with coughs and colds, you could be very surprised to find that germs and viruses no longer seem to pick on you! If every day seems like a long, tiring slog, with no time for fun, you will be astonished when you are able to pack a whole lot more time for yourself into each 24 hours.

Susan Smith (whose picture is on the back cover of this book), from South Shields, started the diet back in January 1991. She weighed in at 10 stone 3lb (64kg), which is not excessively overweight for her height of 5ft 4½in (1.6m). However, Susan is an asthma sufferer, who was even allergic to her 12-year-old daughter's horse! She wanted to lose some weight and get fitter, hoping it would help her cope with her asthma problem, and improve her general health and fitness level.

Now Susan, who is 36 but looks 10 years younger, keeps her weight at a steady 8½ stone (54kg) and is so fit that she finds time for five fitness classes each week, and regularly runs in half-marathons. Her latest was the Great North Run, which she completed in just 2 hours 11 minutes. She also works as a laboratory technician, so has a very busy life. She says: 'I now have so much more energy. I haven't had to use my inhaler for months, and I can actually cuddle my daughter's horse.'

Norah Marshall, 61, from Washington, Tyne and Wear, who works as a night nurse, started the Fatfield Diet in July 1991. She weighed in at 15 stone 4lb (97kg) and lost 1 stone 4lb (8kg) in just two months. She is still losing weight at the rate of 2lb (1kg) weekly. She says: 'I was getting bigger all the time and feeling low. I had no control over my food intake. Some days, I would have a big meal before going on duty then eat chocolates given to me by my patients! I thought my working hours were to blame for my weight. Now, I feel younger and fitter. People have remarked on how much better I look. The beauty of the diet is that it is so adaptable.'

To prove how adaptable the Fatfield Diet is, here are three new versions of the basic plan. They have all been tried and tested by slimmers in the 50-strong Fatfield village slimming group, with excellent results.

THE PLATEAU DIET

Perhaps you've been slimming successfully for some time, but still have a stone or so to lose? Or maybe you have slimmed down, and fattened up so many times that your poor old body is conserving calories like mad instead of burning them off?

You're probably frustrated, fed up and were ready to give up the fight until you spotted this book. Well done! The good news is that you *can* lose those extra pounds and get off that slimming 'plateau'.

During our Fatfield slim-in for the BBC 'Bazaar' programme, a few of our slimmers experienced exactly the same problem. They had lost weight slowly but surely (the best way!) for several months, but suddenly found that no weight-loss registered at our weekly weigh-ins. Although one week at 'stalemate' can easily be explained by fluid changes in the body, when it continues for three or four weeks, something is obviously amiss. To check that there is no cheating going on, we ask all our slimmers to fill in a log of everything they eat each week. This is a good idea for anyone who seriously wants to slim. Even if there is no-one to check your log except you, you will be able to pinpoint any weak spots and also those conveniently forgotten moments when you pinched two glacé cherries off the cake you made for your mother-in-law, or stole a Marmite butty from the baby! Men who fill in their weekly logs are often astonished to find that 50 per cent of their daily calories have been consumed in the pub!

At Fatfield, our slimmers bring their log each week for a talk-through with myself or my assistant, Toni. When we examined the logs of our 'plateau' people carefully, we found that they had not been cheating. So, I devised a special diet to help rev up their sluggish metabolism and encourage their bodies to start 'burning' calories again. Here's how it works:

Week One is a maintenance plan of 1500 calories designed to give the body a 'holiday' from dieting. It is divided up into four meals instead of the usual three, to liven up your system. During this week you should aim to walk briskly for one hour each day.

Week Two is a split-calorie plan which allows 900 calories for three days, then 1200 calories for four days. This helps to 'shock' the system into action. Although it sounds very low in calories, this week's foods are carefully chosen to pack as much bulk in as possible, so you never feel hungry. Exercise this week should be increased to one hour's walking, plus a gentle aerobic activity such as swimming two or three times a week.

The two Weeks are repeated alternately, until the weight starts moving again. Then, one of the 10 original diet plans explained in *The Fatfield Diet* can be chosen, according to your weight, sex and lifestyle.

WEEK ONE

CALORIES About 1500 daily for women, 1700 for men and women with more than 3 stone (19kg) to lose.

EVERY DAY You can have ½pt (275ml) skimmed milk for your tea and coffee and unlimited water and mineral water. Use artificial sweeteners only.

FREE VEGETABLES Choose from the list on page 7. Eat as much as you can.

MEN (and women with more than 3 stone (19kg) to lose) You can have 2 extra slices of wholemeal bread daily, with a little low-fat spread.

NOW CHOOSE Each day choose one Breakfast, two Light Meals, one Main Meal and one Treat. (Eat one of the Light Meals at lunchtime, and the other whenever suits you – mid-morning, as a snack when you come home from a hard day's work with your tummy rumbling away or even during the evening when you are watching TV.) Vary your meal choices to give you a super variety of nutrients. This is a 'lenient' week, so you can eat out or have a takeaway!

BREAKFASTS (choose *one* each day)

- 1 poached egg, grilled tomatoes, 1 slice of wholemeal toast, watercress and cucumber

- Blackberry and Apple Sundae (*see* recipe, page 42)
- Fisherman's Breakfast (*see* recipe, page 41)
- ½ grapefruit or slice of melon, 1oz (25g) unsweetened cereal with milk from allowance, 2 crispbreads with 1 teaspoon marmalade
- 2 slices of wholemeal toast topped with grilled tomatoes and 1 rasher grilled streaky bacon, watercress or cucumber slices
- ½ medium melon, sliced across with seeds scooped out. Fill the cavity with 2 tablespoons natural, low-fat yogurt, ½oz (15g) muesli and 1 small banana, sliced
- 1 slice of toast topped with 1 small can (5oz/125g) baked beans, grilled tomatoes

LIGHT MEALS (choose *two* each day)

Don't forget to add huge mixed salads and vegetables from the 'free' list on page 7.

- Tuna Bake (*see* recipe, page 51), medium banana
- Cheese and Apple Toast (*see* recipe, page 51), 1 carton Diet Ski or Shape Yogurt, 1 pear
- Courgettes with Haricot Beans or Au Gratin (*see* recipes, pages 128 and 132), 3 tablespoons plain boiled rice, 1 small carton Shape Sundae
- Any Lean Cuisine slimmer's meal, plus 1 apple, pear or orange
- Mixed Vegetable Casserole (*see* recipe, page 126), 10oz (275g) chicken leg (no skin, roasted or grilled), a few grapes
- *Sandwiches* Allow 2 slices of wholemeal bread with filling of salad from the free list (page 7) and one of these:

17

- 2oz (50g) lean ham or chicken (no skin) with 1 teaspoon sweet pickle

- 4oz (100g) cottage cheese with chives

- 1 large mashed banana with a sprinkling of cinnamon

- 3 orange slices and 1 tablespoon Shape Soft Cheese. Add 1 can (10.4oz/295g) Weight Watchers from Heinz soup

- *Baked potatoes* Allow 1 10oz (275g) potato, scrubbed and baked, with one of these toppings:

  - 1 small carton (5oz/150g) natural, low-fat yogurt with sprinkling of curry powder and lemon juice

  - 2 tablespoons baked beans, sliced tomatoes

  - 1 small carton (5oz/150g) Shape Coleslaw salad

  - 1 small can (8oz/227g) tomatoes with 2oz (50g) chopped prawns or shrimps

- *Cold platter* Salad from 'free' list (page 7) with sliced, hard-boiled egg, 2 tablespoons sweetcorn, 1 carton (4oz/100g) cottage cheese with chives or pineapple, onion rings, orange slices, 2 teaspoons raisins

- *Cereal meals* Choose from the following:

  - 2 Weetabix, milk from allowance, 1 large sliced banana

  - 1oz (25g) unsweetened muesli, milk from allowance, 1 Diet Ski yogurt, any flavour, 1 slice of wholemeal toast with 1 teaspoon marmalade

  - 1oz (25g) porridge oats, made up with water, milk from allowance, 1 slice of wholemeal toast topped with sliced tomatoes, 1 Shape Sundae, any flavour

MAIN MEALS (choose *one* each day)

Don't forget your 'free' vegetables (page 7).

Home Cooked

- Bangers and Mash with Onion, Mushroom and Tomato Gravy (*see* recipe, page 57), 3oz (75g) peas
- Beef Stew with Newcastle Brown Ale, 5oz (150g) baked potato, 1 medium banana
- Spaghetti Bolognese (*see* recipe, page 98)
- 3oz (75g) roast, lean meat, 3oz (75g) dry roast potatoes (par-boil, brush lightly with vegetable oil and brown under the grill), Slimmers' Apple Bread Pudding (*see* recipe, page 144)
- 6oz (175g) any white fish, grilled with lemon juice and sliced tomatoes, 8oz (225g) baked potato, baked apple
- 1 well-grilled beefburger or vegeburger, 3oz (75g) oven chips, 1 small can (7.6oz/215g) spaghetti-in-tomato sauce, grilled tomatoes, 1 small scoop vanilla icecream

Ready Meals and Takeaways

- Any Findus Lean Cuisine meal with 8oz (225g) baked potato and 1 apple or orange to follow
- Tandoori Chicken, 3 tablespoons plain boiled rice and 1 small banana to follow
- Ross Stir Fry Chinese Chicken or Mexican Beef Chilli with 3 tablespoons plain boiled rice and 1 apple, orange or pear to follow
- Any Sainsbury's Healthy Cuisine Meal except Chicken Madras with Turmeric Rice and 1 apple, orange or pear to follow
- Haddock in Batter from chippie, with unlimited vegetables and salad only

Restaurants

- Carvery: Melon cocktail, roast chicken and unlimited vegetables
- Chinese: Prawn Chop Suey and 2 tablespoons plain boiled rice
- Indian: Chicken Tikka, 2 tablespoons plain boiled rice, 1 poppadum
- Steak House: 6oz (175g) fillet or rump steak, 1 small baked potato with no topping

TREATS (choose *one* each day)

- 1 glass of dry wine
- 2 'short' drinks (pub measure) with low-calorie mixers only
- ½pt (275ml) beer or lager (not strong lager)
- 1 fun size Mars or Snickers bar
- 1 small digestive biscuit

WEEK TWO

CALORIES Three days at 900 calories, four days at 1200 calories. (1100 and 1400 calories for men or women with more than 3 stone/19kg to lose).

EVERY DAY ½pt (275ml) skimmed milk for your tea and coffee, unlimited water and mineral water. Use artificial sweeteners only.

FREE VEGETABLES Choose from the list on page 7. Eat as much as you can.

MEN (and women with more than 3 stone/19kg to lose) Add 2 slices of wholemeal bread, ½pt (275ml) beer or lager or 1 glass dry wine.

NOW CHOOSE Each day choose one Breakfast, one Light Meal, one Main Meal and one Treat.

BREAKFASTS (choose *one* each day)

- 1 small glass unsweetened orange juice, 1 slice of wholemeal toast with Marmite, 1 apple
- 1 small wholemeal roll with 1 rasher grilled back bacon and grilled tomatoes
- 1 small carton (5oz/150g) natural, low-fat yogurt whizzed in the blender with 1 tablespoon wheatgerm, 1 large banana
- 2 crispbreads, grilled tomatoes, 2oz (50g) mushrooms poached in water, 1 poached egg, watercress
- ½ grapefruit, grilled with a pinch of cinnamon on top, 1 slice of wholemeal toast with 1 teaspoon honey, 1 Diet Ski yogurt, any flavour
- 1oz (25g) any unsweetened cereal, milk from allowance, sliced apple, small glass unsweetened tomato or pineapple juice

FIRST THREE DAYS

It is very important to eat plenty of your 'free' vegetables (page 7). Make sure you always sit down to a huge plateful of food at lunchtime and suppertime and don't forget your daily 'treat'.

LIGHT MEALS (choose *one* each day)

Quick, cold meals

- 1 crispy roll with filling of salad and one of these:

21

- 1oz (25g) grated Edam cheese, sliced tomatoes
- 2 tablespoons cottage cheese mixed with 1 teaspoon sweet pickle
- 2oz (50g) lean ham or chicken (no skin)
- Chopped hard-boiled egg mixed with 1 dessertspoon natural, low-fat yogurt and a pinch of curry powder.

Follow with 1 apple, orange, pear, small banana, or 2 medium plums or 10 grapes

- Lemon Dip with Fruit Crudités (*see* recipe, page 45), ½ packet low-fat crisps for dunking
- Pasta Salad (*see* recipe, page 44), crusty wholemeal roll

Soup meals

- 1 can (10.4oz/295g) Weight Watchers from Heinz soup, any flavour, with crusty roll (fill with salad from 'free' list), 1 Harvest Crunch Bar
- Chilled Gazpacho (*see* recipe, page 100), 1 slice of wholemeal bread or toast, 1 carton Shape Coleslaw
- 1 can Heinz Big Soup, any flavour, 2 crispbreads
- 1 can Sainsbury's Gourmet Crab Bisque, 1 slice of wholemeal bread or toast

Cooked Meals

- Cheesey Fish Snack (*see* recipe, page 51), Diet Ski yogurt, any flavour
- Cheese and Vegetable Stir Fry (*see* recipe, page 122), 1 large banana
- Braised Red Cabbage with Apple Cheese (*see* recipe, page 127), 1 apple, orange or small banana

MAIN MEALS (choose *one* each day)

- 1 5oz (150g) lean lamb chop, grilled, 3oz (75g) mashed potato (made with skimmed milk from allowance), thin gravy

- Large slice melon or ½ grapefruit, any Lean Cuisine Meal (don't forget the huge portion of 'free' vegetables and salad)

- Well-grilled beefburger, 2 tablespoons baked beans, grilled tomatoes, 2oz (50g) mushrooms poached in water, 1 rasher well-grilled streaky bacon, 2 crispbreads

- 8oz (225g) chicken joint, roast or grilled with skin removed, 2 tablespoons sweetcorn or peas, 1 small crusty wholemeal roll

- Onions Stuffed with Baked Beans (*see* recipe, page 131), 3 tablespoons plain boiled rice, a few grapes

- Pork Chop with Rosemary and Orange Sauce (*see* recipe, page 72), 1 tablespoon sweetcorn or peas

- Baked Stuffed Aubergine (*see* recipe, page 106), 3 tablespoons plain boiled rice, 1 scoop vanilla icecream with sauce made from 1 teaspoon jam and hot water

- 6oz (175g) any white fish, grilled with tomatoes, onions, 5oz (150g) baked potato topped with 2 tablespoons natural, low-fat yogurt

TREATS (choose *one* each day)

- 1 Jaffa Cake
- 2 Rich Tea fingers
- Half packet of Polos or Polo Fruits

NEXT FOUR DAYS
LIGHT MEALS (choose *one* each day)

Quick, Cold Meals

- Chicken and Vegetable Salad (*see* recipe, page 46), 1 Diet Ski yogurt and a few grapes
- Sandwich of two slices of wholemeal bread *or* two small crispy rolls with salad and one of these fillings:
  - 2 sardines, drained and mashed with lemon juice, 1 tablespoon natural, low-fat yogurt, diced cucumber, red and green peppers
  - 1 pear cored and sliced, lemon juice, 1oz (25g) chopped lean ham
  - 1oz (25g) grated Edam with 1 teaspoon sweet pickle

  Add 1 apple, orange, pear or small banana.

Soup Meals

- Any Cross and Blackwell Chunky Soup with 1 small wholemeal roll
- St Michael Cream of Chicken, Chunky Beef and Vegetable or Lentil and Bacon Soup with 2 crispbreads
- Homemade soup: use 1 large can (14oz/397g) tomatoes, 1oz (25g) leftover cold chicken or lean ham, chopped vegetables from 'free' list and 1 tablespoon peas. Cook until the vegetables are tender and serve with 1 crusty wholemeal roll and follow with an apple, orange, pear or small banana

Baked Potato Meals

- Cook 1 10oz (275g) baked potato, and top with one of the following (don't forget that 'free' salad):
- 2 tablespoons natural, low-fat yogurt and ½oz (15g) grated Edam cheese

- 2 tablespoons baked beans and chopped tomato
- 4 tablespoons cottage cheese with chives

Cooked Meals

- Well-grilled beefburger, grilled tomatoes, 2oz (50g) mushrooms poached in water, 1 small can (7.6oz/215g) spaghetti-in-tomato sauce, 1 apple
- 1 slice of wholemeal toast topped with 1 small can (8oz/225g) baked beans, ½oz (15g) grated Edam cheese
- Poached egg on 1 slice of wholemeal toast, grilled tomatoes, large banana

MAIN MEALS (choose *one* each day)

- Any of the meals for First Three Days (page 23), with the addition of 1 crusty roll, 1 slice of wholemeal bread or 2 tablespoons plain boiled rice. Or, choose one of the following:
- Liver, Chipolata and Bean Casserole (*see* recipe, page 56), 2 tablespoons peas, 5oz (150g) baked potato
- Gammon Steaks with Pineapple and Mustard Sauce (*see* recipe, page 65), 3oz (75g) mashed potato (use skimmed milk from allowance for mashing), 2 tablespoons sweetcorn, 1 Diet Ski yogurt, any flavour
- Any Findus Lean Cuisine ready-meal, with 2 pieces of fresh fruit (apple, orange, pear, small banana, 2 plums or 1 large slice of melon) to follow
- 3oz (75g) any cooked, lean meat or 6oz (175g) any grilled white fish with 3oz (75g) mashed potato (use skimmed milk from allowance), 2 tablespoons peas, thin gravy (for meat only, make it with a stock cube), with a frozen mousse to follow

Eating Out

Try to avoid it this week (you've got next week to look forward to!), but if you must eat out choose one of these:

- Indian: Tandoori chicken, 2 tablespoons plain boiled rice
- Chinese: Prawn chop suey, 2 tablespoons plain boiled rice
- McDonald's: Cheeseburger, small orange juice
- Carvery: Melon, roast chicken and vegetables, fruit sorbet

TREATS (choose *two* each day)

- ½pt (275ml) beer or lager
- 1 glass of dry wine
- 2 'short' drinks (pub measure) with low-calorie mixers only
- 1 fun size Mars or Snickers bar
- 1 carton Diet Ski yogurt, any flavour
- 1 piece fresh fruit
- 1 individual meringue nest topped with ½ tablespoon low-fat fromage frais and 2oz (50g) strawberries or raspberries

THE CURRY DIET

From time to time, the Fatfield slimmers ask me to provide a short-term diet that caters for a specific food passion! I am happy to do this, provided that the diet follows the basic eat-more-weigh-less principle of the plan and provided it is a short-term diet which doesn't allow the slimmer to fall into the trap of eating the same foods all the time. That, as every Fatfield slimmer knows by now, is bad for your health as well as unlikely to help you slim. A varied diet will provide more nutrients than a boring one! You'll also be less likely to give up!

This 1250/1500 calorie programme was originally devised for a husband and wife slimming team who wanted to lose a few pounds each before going on holiday. Like an increasing number of people, they just love eating curry, and they felt that their waistlines were expanding because of this habit.

It's easy to see why curry lovers put on weight. Normally, people eat a curry as a late-night extra. So, unless they starve all day (which is not a good idea) that day's calorie intake is increased by an enormous amount. Then, after a big blow-out, they go to bed on a very full tummy, which is the quickest way to put on weight.

So, where do the extra calories come from? Well, an average portion of Meat Madras (540 calories), with a couple of chapatis (140 calories each), some pilau rice (470 calories) and 2 tablespoons of mango chutney (80 calories each) add up to 1450 calories. That's enough for a whole day's meals!

On the Fatfield Curry Diet, you can still eat out at Indian restaurants, or you can prepare your own spicy meals at home. The supermarkets now stock so many curry-flavoured ready-meals, canned vegetables and ingredients that it is simple to whip up tasty Indian-style dishes.

EVERY DAY You may have ½pt (275ml) skimmed milk for your tea and coffee and unlimited water (drink lots!). Use artificial sweeteners only.

MEN (and women with more than 3 stone/19kg to lose) You can have 2 extra poppadums or 1 chapati, plus ½pt (275ml) of lager every day!

FREE VEGETABLES Choose them from the list on page 7. Eat plenty. If you like, spice up salads with a dash of paprika or other spices in the Fatfield Dressings (*see* recipes, page 53). You can also add spices and curry powder to 'free' vegetables like canned tomatoes, courgettes, green beans or cauliflower to make a basic vegetable curry that is *free*. Eat as much as you like.

CALORIES About 1250 daily for women, 1500 for men and women with more than 3 stone (19kg) to lose.

NOW CHOOSE Each day choose one Breakfast, one Lunch, one Supper and one Treat. NB: All rice is the plain boiled type.

BREAKFASTS (choose *one* each day)

- ½ can (8oz/225g) Heinz Curried Beans with Sultanas, 1 slice of wholemeal toast, 1 small apple
- 5fl oz (150ml) unsweetened orange juice, 1 large slice of wholemeal toast with a little low-fat spread and 2 teaspoons ginger preserve
- 1oz (25g) porridge made with water, milk from allowance, 1 small carton (5oz/150g) natural, low-fat yogurt with 2 teaspoons mango chutney stirred in
- 1 egg, boiled and shelled, topped with sauce made from ½ large can (14oz/397g) tomatoes, 1 teaspoon curry powder with 1 slice of wholemeal toast

LUNCHES (choose *one* each day)

- 1 can (6½oz/185g) John West Tuna in Curry sauce, large mixed salad, 1 poppadum
- 1 can St Michael Vegetable Curry, 2oz (50g) cold chicken (no skin), 1 banana

- Curry sandwich: 2 slices of wholemeal bread spread with 3oz (75g) cottage cheese, a pinch of curry powder and sliced cucumber, 1 small carton natural, low-fat yogurt with 1 dessertspoon mango chutney stirred in

- Takeaway: 1 portion Tandoori chicken, huge mixed salad with lemon dressing, a few grapes

- 1 pot Golden Wonder Chicken Curry Meal, cucumber and tomato salad, 1 apple, 2 crispbreads

- 1 Sainsbury's Onion Bhagia with ½ can (16oz/425g) Sainsbury's Chilli beans in Chilli sauce, huge mixed salad

SUPPERS (choose *one* each day)

At home

- Findus Chicken Korma Ready Meal, large mixed salad and cucumber raita (mix 2 tablespoons natural, low-fat yogurt with cucumber slices and lemon juice to taste) (*see* also recipe, page 86)

- Tesco Chicken Vindaloo with Pilau Rice, large green salad, a few grapes

- Sainsbury Vegetable Dhansak, 2 tablespoons plain boiled rice, 1 apple or orange

- Ross Indian Chicken Stir-Fry, 2 tablespoons plain boiled rice, large mixed salad with lemon juice dressing, 1 pear

- Quick Keema (*see* recipe, page 87), 2 tablespoons plain boiled rice, sliced apple, cucumber and celery salad with lemon juice and sprinkling of chilli powder, 1 banana baked with pinch of ginger

- Fruity Quorn Curry (*see* recipe, page 123), 4 tablespoons plain boiled rice, 1 small carton (5oz/150g) natural, low-fat yogurt with sliced cucumber and lemon juice

- 1 10oz (275g) chicken leg (skin removed), grilled or roast with sauce made from large portion 'free' vegetables flavoured with spices and curry powder to taste, 6oz (175g) baked potato
- 6oz (175g) any white fish, baked or grilled with sliced tomatoes, onion, lemon juice and paprika, 1 small can (8oz/225g) Heinz Curried Beans, vegetables and salad from 'free' list (page 7)

At the curry house

- Chicken tikka (as Main Course), 2 tablespoons pilau rice, 2 tablespoons cucumber raita
- Tandoori chicken, green salad, 1 chapati
- Mixed vegetable curry, green salad

TREATS (choose *one* each day)

- 1 glass of dry wine
- ½pt (275ml) beer or lager (or save it up for Friday night)
- 1 pack KP Poppadums
- 1 poppadum with 2 tablespoons natural, low-fat yogurt and dash of curry powder for dunking

THE COUPLES' DIET

The Fatfield Diet is fine for whole families, because the meals are so filling. All you have to do is add extra helpings of the more calorie-intensive foods like meat and cheese for non-slimmers. You will probably end up eating bigger platefuls than they do because you'll have unlimited vegetables from your 'free' list (page 7).

If you have a partner who is as anxious to lose weight as you are, it is a good idea to slim together. Then, you can encourage each other all the way. This diet was created for couples who enjoy delicious food, but haven't a lot of time to prepare it. The suppers (or lunches, see below) are slightly higher in calories than usual to allow for man-sized appetites and to make your main meal together special.

While you're following the diet, take up a sport or go to exercise classes together. If either of you is very over-weight, he or she should check with their doctor before embarking on a fitness programme. Give your partner an incentive with a gift or outing for every 7lb (3kg) lost. Keep an eye on each other at parties or when you are both out with friends. Have a special code – a pinch, tickle or wink – which means 'Stop, you're eating, or drinking too much!'.

The diet can also be followed by a lone slimmer, but do invite a friend around to share some of the delicious lunches and suppers!

EVERY DAY You can have ½pt (275ml) skimmed milk for your tea and coffee, and unlimited water. Use artificial sweeteners only.

FREE VEGETABLES Choose from the list on page 7. Don't forget to stock up with frozen vegetables in case you are both too busy to go to the shops or market. Remember that it is great fun to shop together, and less tiring than trying to do it alone. My husband Patrick and I are both dedicated slimmers. We do our bulk shopping every fortnight, and reward ourselves afterwards with a slap-up, low-calorie meal – often the Moules Marinières dish on page 96, with fresh mussels from the local fish stall. We add a huge mixed salad, some crusty bread and still have calories left for a glass of dry white wine each!

MEN Add 2 extra slices of wholemeal bread and ½pt (275ml) beer or lager each day.

CALORIES About 1200 daily for women and 1500 for men (or women with more than 3 stone/19kg to lose).

NOW CHOOSE Each day choose one Breakfast, one Lunch, one Supper and one Treat. You may swap around the Lunch and Supper meals if you normally eat your main meal at lunchtime.

BREAKFASTS (choose *one* each day)

- Large slice melon with ginger, 1 poached egg on toast, grilled tomatoes
- 1oz (25g) any unsweetened cereal, milk from allowance, 1 large banana
- Fruity Breakfast Roll (*see* recipe, page 41)
- 5fl oz (150ml) unsweetened orange juice with 1 glass of dry sparkling wine, 2 crispbreads spread with 1 teaspoon strawberry or raspberry jam
- 2 slices of wholemeal toast topped with 2 tablespoons cottage cheese, and a few grapes
- 1 Weetabix biscuit with milk from allowance, 1 sliced pear, 1 slice of wholemeal toast with 1 teaspoon marmalade

LUNCHES (choose *one* each day)

- Cottage Baked Potato with Minty Tomato Salad (*see* recipe, page 49)
- Sandwich of 2 slices of wholemeal bread with any of the fillings from the Fantastic Fatfield Fillings list on page

50 plus 2 pieces of the following fresh fruit: apple, orange, medium slice melon, small banana, 2 large plums, 10 grapes, ½ mango or 1 nectarine

- 2 medium wholemeal rolls with filling of salad from 'free' list plus two of the following:
  - 1oz (25g) grated low-fat Cheddar cheese with 1 teaspoon sweet pickle
  - 1 sliced apple, lemon juice and 1 tablespoon Shape Soft Cheese
  - 2oz (50g) lean, cooked ham or chicken (skin removed)
- 1 small can slimmer's soup, any flavour, 4oz (100g) any grilled white fish or shellfish, huge mixed salad from 'free' list, 5oz (150g) baked potato
- 2 eggs, beaten with 1 dessertspoon skimmed milk, salt and freshly ground black pepper, cooked as an open omelette in a heavy-based, non-stick pan with just a little oil or butter, with a filling of 4oz (100g) frozen mixed vegetables and ½oz (15g) grated Edam cheese
- Gazpacho (*see* recipe, page 100), 1 crusty wholemeal roll with salad from 'free' list (page 7) and 1oz (25g) Edam cheese or 2oz (50g) cold turkey or chicken (skin removed), 1 apple
- 4oz (100g) cottage cheese mixed with 2oz (50g) peeled prawns, ¼ cucumber peeled and diced, 2oz (50g) canned asparagus, drained and chopped. Serve, seasoned with freshly ground black pepper on a bed of lettuce leaves, plus 1 5oz (150g) baked potato

SUPPERS (choose *one* each day)

- Lovers' Dinner (*see* recipes, pages 71–2), 1 glass of dry wine

- 5oz (150g) lean rump steak, 3oz (75g) McCain Oven chips, vegetables and salad from 'free' list (page 7), 1 scoop vanilla icecream with 1 teaspoon jam diluted with 1 tablespoon unsweetened orange juice
- Low Calorie Fish and Chips (*see* recipe, page 66), ½pt (275ml) lager or glass of dry white wine, huge mixed salad from 'free' list (page 7), a few grapes
- Moules Marinières (*see* recipe, page 96), 4oz (100g) chicken breast poached in 1 can slimmer's mushroom or chicken soup, vegetables from 'free' list, 3oz (75g) mashed potatoes made with skimmed milk, baked apple
- Hummus (*see* recipe, page 107), 2 crispbreads, Cheese and Vegetable Stir Fry (*see* recipe, page 122), 1 crusty wholemeal roll, 1oz (25g) low-fat Cheddar cheese
- 3oz (75g) any lean roast meat, thin gravy, huge pile of vegetables from 'free' list (page 7), 3oz (75g) large chunk or chunks of roast potato (cooked the Fatfield Way, see page 61), 2oz (50g) carrots, Apricot and Yogurt Icecream (*see* recipe, page 139), or 1 Diet Ski yogurt, any flavour, and 1 apple or orange

TREATS (choose *one* each day)
- 1 glass of dry wine
- ½pt (275ml) beer or lager
- 2 'short' drinks (pub measure) with low-calorie mixers
- 1 fun size Mars or Snickers bar
- Chabourcy Creme Caramel
- Shape Sundae and a few grapes
- Ambrosia Pot Low Fat Rice
- 2 Jaffa Cakes

CHAPTER THREE

BREAKFASTS
IN A HURRY

No time for breakfast? On the Fatfield Diet, you should definitely *make* time for an early morning meal. But, you certainly don't have to spend hours slaving over a hot stove, or get up at dawn. In fact, if you truly can't face eating before you leave home to go to work, you can pack up your breakfast and take it with you.

Traditionally, we tend to eat either a sketchy snack of cereals or toast, or a huge, cooked breakfast. The first is certainly better than nothing, but the second can be packed with fat and calories and hardly ideal for slimmers.

Here's a selection of recipes which provide a tasty, appetizing start to the day, for a very small number of calories. The cooked dishes are so quick to prepare that you can serve them up in less than 10 minutes. The cold meals can be prepared the night before, or placed in an airtight container to pack into your shopping bag or brief-case. If you are really rushed, a blender is a useful gadget for whizzing up quick, nourishing breakfasts with yogurt, fruit and juices. Storecupboard breakfast basics include muesli, bran and yogurt.

On the Continent, cheese and meat are breakfast basics – both can be tasty so long as they are combined with something refreshing such as citrus fruit or tomatoes, and you don't overdo the portion sizes.

Although we don't usually think of serving salad greens

at breakfast time, it is worth keeping some washed watercress in the fridge to add a spot of colour and extra iron to your breakfast meal.

In this chapter all the recipes are for one person only, as in most households people tend to 'do their own' thing at breakfast time.

CHEESEY TOMATOES ON TOAST

Serves: 1
Calories per serving: 250

2 slices wholemeal toast
2 large tomatoes, sliced
4 tbsp cottage cheese
Watercress to garnish

1. Toast one side of each slice of wholemeal bread under the grill.
2. Transfer to an ovenproof dish, untoasted side up. Place the sliced tomatoes on top of the bread. Return to the grill until the tomatoes are soft.
3. Place 2 tablespoons cottage cheese on top of each slice, and garnish with watercress. I like this with loads of Worcestershire sauce!

SWEETCORN GRILL

Serves: 1
Calories per serving: 235

3oz (75g) canned sweetcorn, drained
1oz (25g) low-fat Cheddar cheese
1 slice wholemeal toast
1 tomato, thinly sliced

1.   Heat the corn and cheese gently in a small saucepan until the cheese melts.
2.   Place on the bread, cover with the slices of tomato and grill until the tomato is cooked.

LIQUID BREAKFAST

Serves: 1
Calories per serving: 160

For a more substantial breakfast that's packed with goodness, pour your drink over a 1oz (25g) portion of any unsweetened cereal and top with chopped fresh fruit. Recommended as a Saturday morning breakfast for footballers or hockey players.

1 small carton (5oz/150g) natural, low-fat yogurt
1 small banana
1 tbsp wheatgerm
2 tbsp unsweetened orange juice
Pinch of cinnamon

1.   Whizz up everything together in a blender, and drink slowly.

SCRAMBLED EGGS WITH MUSHROOMS

Serves: 1
Calories per serving: 235

Mushrooms taste better, look plumper and go further if they are poached in water instead of fried. What's more they only 'cost' 4 calories per 1oz (25g), instead of 50!

2 eggs
2 tbsp skimmed milk
Salt and black pepper
3oz (75g) button mushrooms
Watercress to garnish
2 crispbreads

1.   Beat together the eggs, skimmed milk and season to taste.
2.   Cook over a low heat, stirring all the time or microwave, stirring twice until creamy but *not* overcooked.
3.   Meanwhile, poach the mushrooms whole in a little water for 5 minutes.
4.   Serve the scrambled eggs and mushrooms on a plate with the crispbreads and garnish with watercress.

BUMPER BACON ROLL

Serves: 1
Calories per serving: 310

1 large bap or crispy roll
2oz (50g) streaky bacon
2 tomatoes
Watercress
1oz (25g) sweetcorn

1. Split open the bap or roll.
2. Grill the bacon on a rack until crisp, discarding any fat.
3. Halve the tomatoes and grill, cut side up.
4. Sandwich everything together, adding watercress and sweetcorn. It will be oozy, but delicious!

MELON AND MUESLI FRUIT BASKET

Serves: 1
Calories per serving: 250

½ small Ogen or honeydew melon
1oz (25g) unsweetened muesli
1 red apple, cored and chopped
½ small carton low-fat fruit-flavoured yogurt
A few seedless grapes, chopped
Cinnamon

1. Remove the seeds from the melon. Remove the flesh with a teaspoon making 'ball' shapes or use a melon baller if you have one.
2. Mix the melon flesh with the muesli and chopped apple, and pile back into the shell.
3. Top with the yogurt, chopped grapes and a sprinkling of cinnamon.

BOSTON BAKED BEANS

Serves: 1
Calories per serving: 340

1 small can (5.3oz/150g) baked beans
1 tsp Dijon mustard
1 small can (7oz/200g) tomatoes
2 rashers streaky bacon, grilled on a rack
2 crispbreads

1. Heat the baked beans in a small pan.
2. Add the mustard and tomatoes and heat through.
3. Serve in a bowl with the bacon crumbled on top, and the crispbreads for dunking.

GRAPE AND LEMON CHEESE PITTA

Serves: 1
Calories per serving: 300

Wholemeal pitta bread is super for transporting a scrumptious breakfast to work. Each piece contains just 165 calories – stuff it with a rasher of crispy grilled streaky bacon, sliced tomatoes, lettuce and add an apple for another great early morning meal which 'costs' under 300 calories.

1 pitta bread, split
2oz (50g) Shape Low Fat Soft Cheese
Squeeze of lemon juice
10 seedless grapes

1. Make a pocket along the length of the pitta bread.
2. Mix together the cheese, lemon juice and grapes in a small bowl.
3. Stuff the mixture into the pitta bread. Yum.

FISHERMAN'S BREAKFAST

Serves: 1
Calories per serving: 200

1 McCain fish cake
2 tomatoes, halved
1 dsp tartare sauce
1 tbsp natural, low-fat yogurt
Lettuce, cucumber and watercress
1 slice wholemeal toast
Slice of lemon to garnish

1. Grill the fish cake on both sides until crisp.
2. Grill the tomatoes on a rack, cut side up.
3. Mix together the tartare sauce and yogurt.
4. Place lettuce, cucumber and watercress on a plate and top with the slice of toast and fish cake.
5. Pour the sauce on top and garnish with a slice of lemon.

FRUITY BREAKFAST ROLL

Serves: 1
Calories per serving: 205

1 crusty wholemeal roll
1 apple, cored and chopped
½oz (15g) raisins
1 tbsp lemon juice
1 tbsp cottage cheese or low-fat fromage frais

1. Split the roll.
2. Mix the remaining ingredients together.
3. Pile on to one half of the roll, and place the second half on top.

BLACKBERRY AND APPLE SUNDAE

Serves: 1
Calories per serving: 200

1oz (25g) bran cereal
1 medium apple, cored and chopped
½ small carton low-fat blackcurrant or raspberry yogurt
A few blackberries to garnish

1. Place the cereal in the bottom of a large sundae glass.
2. Mix in the chopped apple.
3. Pour yogurt over the top.
4. Garnish with blackberries.

BANANA SANDWICH WITH HONEY AND YOGURT

Serves: 1
Calories per serving: 260

1 medium banana
2 medium slices wholemeal bread
2 tbsp natural, low-fat yogurt
1 tsp runny honey

1. Slice the banana and place on one piece of bread.
2. Pour over the yogurt, and drizzle honey on top.
3. Place the second slice of bread on top, cut the sandwich in half and serve.

CHAPTER FOUR

PACKED LUNCHES, SNACKS AND NAUGHTY NIBBLES

If you really want to take control of your weight, you must never get caught short without the right kind of snack food. Fast food joints are everywhere – and they're just waiting for slimmers with rumbling tums to wander in. On the Fatfield diet, you eat so much – including between-meals snacks – that you should never be hungry. So, make sure that you have a good stock of fruit, salad vegetables, and low-calorie supermarket goodies like slimmer's fromage frais, yogurt, and soups. Work out when your danger times are, and be prepared. For instance, if you're always ravenous when you get home from work and start preparing the evening meal, nibble a low-calorie snack then, to stave off the hunger pangs.

It's always a good idea to take a packed lunch to work. That way, you won't be tempted by canteen chips. In this chapter, there's a really super selection of interesting packed meals. Invest in a set of good airtight containers and a small vacuum flask, and add pretty paper napkins, so your midday break becomes a feast.

Late-night telly watching often brings on an attack of the naughty nibbles, particularly if you are watching a food or drink commercial. The answer is to whizz up a treat from our suggestions, rather than digging into the biscuit tin.

PASTA SALAD

Serves: 1
Calories per serving: 180

You can use any leftovers such as chicken, green beans, tuna, broccoli or melon balls with this easy salad. If you add a crusty wholemeal roll, and follow with a piece of fresh fruit, you'll have a satisfying lunch at around 350 calories.

2oz (50g) cooked pasta twists, cooled
1oz (25g) Edam cheese, cut into ½in (1cm) cubes
½ small green pepper, cored, deseeded and sliced
½ small red pepper, cored, deseeded and sliced
1 tbsp low-fat fromage frais
Curry powder to taste

1. Mix the pasta, cheese and slices of pepper in a bowl.
2. To make the dressing blend the fromage frais with curry powder to taste.
3. Combine the dressing with the pasta salad.

LEMON DIP WITH FRUIT CRUDITÉS

Serves: 4
Calories per serving: About 200

4oz (100g) Edam cheese, grated finely
2 tbsp boiling water
6oz (175g) low-fat fromage frais
Juice and grated rind of ½ small lemon
¼ tsp ground ginger
Fruit crudités
1 large green and 1 large red apple, cored and cut into
    segments, dipped in lemon juice
A few grapes, pineapple chunks (canned in juice), sliced
    kiwi fruit or mango

1.   Place the grated Edam in a bowl, add the boiling water and stir.
2.   Add the fromage frais, lemon juice and rind and ground ginger to make a dip.
3.   Spoon the dip into a glass dish and chill for 30 minutes.
4.   Arrange the fruit crudités decoratively on a serving plate, with the dip in the centre. For a packed lunch, put ¼ of the dip in a small airtight container, and pack a selection of fruit separately.

CHICKEN AND VEGETABLE SALAD

Serves: 2
Calories per serving: 215

½ small cauliflower
4oz (100g) carrots, sliced thinly
4oz (100g) frozen green beans
2oz (50g) frozen peas
4oz (100g) canned sweetcorn
1 celery stick, chopped finely
4oz (100g) cooked chicken, skin removed and diced
Chopped parsley to garnish
Dressing
4 tbsp natural, low-fat yogurt
½ tsp horseradish sauce
½ tsp lemon juice

1. Break the cauliflower into florets.
2. Cook the cauliflower, carrots, beans and peas in boiling salted water for 5 minutes. Drain.
3. Mix all the vegetables and the diced chicken together in a bowl.
4. Mix together the dressing ingredients and pour over the salad. Toss well, garnish with parsley and serve, or pack in an airtight container.

TOMATO, CARROT AND ONION SOUP

Serves: 2
Calories per serving: 90

Use canned chopped tomatoes as a base for other filling soups. Just add leftover vegetables, chopped finely, or even a few leftover prawns or strips of ham. This particular recipe also tastes great chilled and travels well in a wide-necked vacuum flask (take the yogurt separately and eat the rest with a chopped apple as your pud!).

1 large can (14oz/397g) chopped tomatoes
2 large carrots, grated
1 small onion, chopped finely
½pt (275ml) chicken stock
1 tsp dried basil
Pinch of nutmeg
Salt and black pepper
2 tbsp natural, low-fat yogurt
Chopped parsley to garnish

1.   Place the tomatoes in a large saucepan.
2.   Add the carrot, onion, stock, basil and a pinch of nutmeg.
3.   Bring to the boil, stirring, cover and simmer for 20 minutes. Check the seasoning – add just a touch of salt and ground black pepper if necessary.
4.   Serve with a swirl of yogurt and a sprinkling of parsley on top.

TANGY HAM ON TOAST

Serves: 1
Calories per serving: 210

This is a scrummy lunch for one person. Pile on plenty of 'free' salad vegetables (page 7), and have a juicy peach or pear afterwards.

1 slice wholemeal bread
½ apple, cored and sliced
1oz (25g) lean ham
1 dsp tomato chutney
1 pickled onion, chopped
1oz (25g) grated low-fat Cheddar cheese
Parsley, lettuce, cucumber and watercress to garnish

1.   Toast the bread on both sides.
2.   Arrange the apple slices, then the ham on top of the toast.
3.   Spread the tomato chutney over the ham and sprinkle with onion.
4.   Sprinkle with the grated cheese and place under a hot grill until the cheese is bubbly.
5.   Serve sprinkled with chopped parsley and garnished with salad greens.

COTTAGE BAKED POTATO WITH MINTY TOMATO SALAD

Serves: 1
Calories per serving: 255

1 7oz (200g) baking potato, scrubbed and pricked
2 large tomatoes, sliced
2oz (50g) cottage cheese with chives
Dressing
1 tsp mint sauce
1 dsp wine vinegar

1.   Bake the potato in a moderate oven (400°F, 200°C, gas mark 6), or cook in a microwave oven until cooked through.
2.   Meanwhile, place the sliced tomatoes on a plate, mix together the dressing ingredients and pour on top. Chill the salad until required.
3.   Split the potato, spoon over the cottage cheese, and serve with the salad.

FANTASTIC FATFIELD FILLINGS

Fed up with stuffing your sandwiches, baps and rolls with the same old low-calorie fillings? Here are six mouthwatering ideas, calorie counted. Add an extra 100 calories for your bap or roll, 165 calories if you pop the filling into a warmed wholemeal pitta, or 140 if you use two slices of wholemeal bread to make a sandwich. Don't forget to add plenty of 'free' salad vegetables from the list on page 7, and fresh fruit or a low-fat yogurt for dessert.

1. 2oz (50g) cooked, sliced chicken (no skin), mixed with 2 chopped radishes, diced cucumber and tossed in dressing made from 1 tablespoon reduced-calorie mayonnaise and ½ level teaspoon horseradish sauce. *Calories: 135.*

2. 2oz (50g) low-fat soft cheese mixed with ½oz (15g) raisins, grated carrot, chopped celery and lemon juice. *Calories: 135.*

3. 3oz (75g) baked beans with chopped onion, 1 dessertspoon sweet pickle, 1 teaspoon Dijon mustard and ½oz (15g) grated low-fat Cheddar cheese. *Calories: 120.*

4. 1 pear, cored and sliced, lemon juice, ½oz (15g) chopped lean ham, 1 tablespoon cottage cheese and sprigs of fresh mint. *Calories: 90.*

5. 2 sardines, drained and mashed with lemon juice and 1 tablespoon natural, low-fat yogurt, then mixed with diced cucumber, red and green peppers, cored, deseeded and diced, and freshly ground black pepper. *Calories: 135.*

6. 1 small banana, sliced, mixed with 1 sliced, drained apricot half (canned in juice), lemon juice, ½oz (15g) raisins, 1 dessertspoon low-fat fromage frais and a pinch of grated nutmeg. *Calories: 105.*

CHEAP AND CHEESEY LUNCHES

Our Fatfield slimmers are a hard-working bunch, with many of the women holding down several jobs as well as looking after a family. It's all too tempting to skip meals, but that is a certain way to diet disaster. Here are some quick cheesey lunchtime ideas from Fatfield slimmers Sheila Turnbull and Ann McKenna.

1.   *Tuna Bake:* Drain a 3½oz (99g) can of tuna in brine and pour into an ovenproof dish. Heat 1 can (7½oz/213g) creamed mushrooms and pour on top of the tuna. Mix 2oz (50g) grated low-fat cheese with 2oz (50g) wholemeal breadcrumbs and sprinkle on top. Bake in a moderate oven (350°F, 180°C, gas mark 4) for 10 minutes, then flash under the grill until golden. *Serves 2. Calories per serving: 290.*

2.   *Cheese and Apple Toasts:* Toast one side of a slice of wholemeal bread. Spread the other side with ½ teaspoon French mustard. Peel and thinly slice 1 apple. Place the slices on top of the mustard, squeeze lemon juice on top and top with 1oz (25g) grated Edam cheese. Place under the grill until the cheese melts. *Serves 1. Calories per serving: 215.*

3.   *Cheesey Fish Snack:* Toast one side of a slice of wholemeal bread, and cover the other side with 2oz (50g) cooked smoked cod or haddock and sliced onion. Sprinkle with salt and freshly ground black pepper and 1oz (25g) grated low-fat Cheddar cheese. Grill under a moderate heat to allow the fish to heat through and the cheese to go golden brown. *Serves 1. Calories per serving: 210.*

TELLY NIBBLES

Here are six ideas for sweet or savoury nibbles and drinks. They are for those awful moments when you feel you must have something – or dive into the biscuit tin! They're all very low in calories and very satisfying.

1.   2 Ryvitas, topped with sliced tomato, cucumber and 2 tablespoons Shape coleslaw, and a mug of Oxo to drink. *Calories: 100.*

2.   1 slice wholemeal bread spread with 1 tablespoon Shape Fromage Frais and a mug of Ovaltine Options to drink. *Calories: 120.*

3.   Huge mixed salad topped with sliced pear and 2 tablespoons cottage cheese, washed down with a glass of low-alcohol wine. *Calories: 135.*

4.   1 mug Batchelor's Slim-A-Soup with wholemeal toast croûtons and ½oz (15g) grated Edam cheese on top. *Calories: 115.*

5.   1 carton Shape Fromage Frais mixed with 1 chopped banana and a sprinkling of muesli, and lemon tea to drink. *Calories: 180.*

5.   Open sandwich of 1 slice of slimmer's bread, lettuce, watercress, sliced orange, 2 dates and 1 tablespoon natural low-fat yogurt, and a mug of Bovril to drink. *Calories: 120.*

FATFIELD SALAD DRESSINGS

These are all extra low in calories, and very tasty indeed. Try them, and experiment with your own no-fat versions.

1.   *Yogurt and Lemon:* Mix together a 5oz (150g) carton natural, low-fat yogurt, 2 tbsp lemon juice, 2 tsp chopped fresh herbs such as basil, mint or fennel leaves to taste or ½ tsp dried herbs and freshly ground black pepper. Chill for 1 hour before serving. *Serves 4. Calories per serving: 20.*

2.   *Orange or Lemon Vinaigrette:* Shake together in a screw-topped jar, 3 tbsp wine vinegar, 1 tbsp fresh orange or lemon juice, 1 tbsp grated orange or lemon rind, ½ tsp French mustard and freshly ground black pepper and salt to taste. *Serves 2. Calories per serving: 5.*

3.   *Spicy Tomato Juice Dressing:* Shake together in a screw-topped jar 4 tbsp tomato juice, 4 tbsp wine vinegar, 1 tsp Worcestershire sauce, 2 tsp finely chopped shallots or spring onions, ½ teaspoon dried basil, freshly ground black pepper and salt to taste. *Serves 4. Calories per serving: 5.*

FAVOURITE FATFIELD DRINKS

Got a thirst? Don't just reach for a boring old can of low-calorie fizzy drink. Try these instead:

Minimal Calories

1. *Pink Tonic:* Add a dash of Angostura bitters to a glass of low-calorie tonic water, and garnish with a slice of peach or orange.

2. *Ginger Kick:* Mix 1 tablespoon low calorie lime juice with 1 glass of low-calorie ginger ale, top up with ice and garnish with a slice of lime or lemon and cucumber slices.

3. *Pineapple Crush:* Chop up a few bits of leftover pineapple, canned in juice. Pour on the leftover juice, top up with soda and crushed ice.

4. *Chilled Herbal Teas:* Try making any herbal tea, chilling it, then serving with ice and fresh lemon, orange or grapefruit juice.

Under 100 Calories

1. *Choccy comforter:* Make up one sachet Ovaltine Options Choc-au-lait and serve with an After Eight Mint for dunking.

2. *Spritzer:* Pour out a small glass of white wine, and top up your glass with soda, ice and lemon and a sprig of mint.

3. *Sherry Toddy:* Make up a mug of Bovril and stir in 1 small glass of dry sherry.

CHAPTER FIVE

FAMILY FAVOURITES

The greatest test for any slimmer is sitting down at the table to a big, family meal. For women, it is very hard indeed not to nibble while you're preparing food designed to fill up hungry children and non-slimming men. When the meal finally appears on the table, you really can't be expected to resist tasting it!

On the Fatfield Diet, the family meal is very important indeed. Our slimmers always sit down to a substantial evening meal, and usually serve up exactly the same fare for the family. The subtle differences in the way the dishes are cooked do nothing to impair the taste – they just cut calories and make the meal far healthier, too.

Storecupboard basics for family dishes like these include slimmers' soups (for casseroles and sauces), canned tomatoes, low-fat cheese and natural, low-fat yogurt.

Here are 12 recipes for filling, inexpensive dishes which are all old favourites, with a new, low-calorie twist! Even the Sunday roast is included, plus good old fish and chips!

LIVER, CHIPOLATA AND BEAN CASSEROLE

Serves: 4
Calories per serving: 250

This is the kind of hot, filling supper that it's great to come home to on a winter night, and the calories are so low that you can afford to have a 5oz (150g) baked potato or some noodles to go with it.

4oz (100g) low-fat chipolata sausages
12oz (350g) lamb's liver, sliced thinly
1 onion, sliced
1 can (10.4oz/285g) Weight Watchers from Heinz
    Tomato Soup
2 tsp Worcestershire sauce
1 tsp wine vinegar
1 tsp Dijon mustard
Salt and black pepper
1 medium can (7.9oz/225g) Weight Watchers from Heinz
    Baked Beans
Parsley sprigs to garnish

1.   Grill the sausages on a rack so any fat drips through. When just cooked, cool and cut into 1in (2.5cm) slices.
2.   Place the liver in an ovenproof casserole with the sausages and onion.
3.   Mix the soup with the Worcestershire sauce, vinegar and mustard.
4.   Season to taste and pour over the liver mixture.
5.   Cover and cook in a moderate oven (350°F, 180°C, gas mark 4) for 45 minutes.
6.   Remove from the oven, and stir in the baked beans. Cook for a further 10 minutes and serve, garnished with parsley sprigs.

BANGERS AND MASH WITH ONION, MUSHROOM AND TOMATO GRAVY

Serves: 4
Calories per serving: 310

Add plenty of green vegetables from your 'free' list (page 7), and finish this substantial meal with a baked apple plus a squirt of aerosol cream. Calorie total? Under 400!

8 low-fat pork sausages
1lb (450g) potatoes, peeled weight
1/4pt (150ml) skimmed milk
Salt and black pepper
1 large onion, chopped finely
2oz (50g) button mushrooms, sliced
1 large can (14oz/397g) tomatoes
Pinch of mixed herbs
1 beef stock cube
Parsley sprigs or watercress to garnish

1. Grill the sausages on a rack, so any fat drips through and can be discarded.
2. Meanwhile, slice the potatoes, cook until tender and mash with skimmed milk and a little salt and freshly ground black pepper to taste.
3. To make the gravy place the chopped onion, mushrooms and tomatoes in a pan with the mixed herbs and cook gently for 5 minutes.
4. Dissolve the stock cube in a little water and juice from the tomatoes, then pour back into the gravy and stir. Simmer gently for 2 minutes.
5. Serve with the potatoes piled in the centre of an oval dish, and the sausages and gravy arranged around them. Garnish with sprigs of parsley or watercress.

TANGY CHEESEBURGERS AND BEANS

Serves: 4
Calories per serving: 265

Add a bap if you like, for an authentic burger bar meal, plus a mixed salad and 3oz (75g) oven chips. Calorie total: 450.

12oz (350g) lean minced beef
1 onion, chopped
½oz (15g) bread, as breadcrumbs
1 beef stock cube, crumbled
1 tsp mixed herbs
Salt and black pepper
1 egg, beaten
2oz (50g) mushrooms, chopped
2 tsp horseradish sauce
1oz (25g) grated Edam cheese
1 medium can (7.9oz/225g) Weight Watchers from Heinz
   Baked Beans

1.   Put the minced beef, onion, breadcrumbs, crumbled stock cube, herbs and seasoning in a bowl, and mix.
2.   Add the beaten egg, mix well and divide the mixture into 4 flat round cakes.
3.   Place in a heatproof dish and grill for 4–5 minutes on each side under a medium heat until cooked through.
4.   Carefully remove from the dish, and place on kitchen paper to remove any excess fat. Keep hot until ready to serve.
5.   Poach the mushrooms in a little water until soft. Drain, and stir in the horseradish sauce and season to taste. Spoon the mushrooms over each burger, and top with the grated cheese.
6.   Pop back under a high grill until the cheese is melted.
7.   Serve with the heated baked beans.

BEEF STEW WITH NEWCASTLE BROWN ALE

Serves: 4
Calories per serving: 190

Guaranteed to warm a man's heart, this substantial supper dish can be served with rice, a small baked potato or just a salad. It also reheats and freezes well.

1lb (450g) lean chuck steak, cubed
1 medium onion, sliced
1 carrot, sliced
1 clove garlic, crushed
3oz (75g) button mushrooms
½pt (275ml) Newcastle Brown Ale (or use Guinness for a richer gravy)
1 beef stock cube
1 tsp malt vinegar
Pinch of nutmeg
Salt and black pepper
1 bay leaf
Chopped parsley to garnish

1.   Dry fry the steak in a heavy-based, non-stick pan to seal the meat.
2.   Place in a deep casserole with the onion, carrot, garlic and mushrooms.
3.   Blend the ale with the stock cube, vinegar and a pinch of nutmeg. Season to taste.
4.   Pour the ale over the meat and vegetables in the casserole, and add the bay leaf.
5.   Cover, and cook in a moderate oven (350°F, 170°C, gas mark 4) for 1½ hours or until the meat is tender. Discard the bay leaf.
6.   Serve garnished with chopped parsley.

LAMB'S KIDNEYS IN PIQUANT YOGURT SAUCE

Serves: 4
Calories per serving: About 135

Add lots of 'free' vegetables (page 7), and a medium-sized baked potato, and you'll enjoy a vitamin-, mineral- and fibre-packed supper for under 350 calories.

8 lamb's kidneys (about 1lb/450g)
5fl oz (150ml) beef stock
4oz (100g) mushrooms, sliced
1 tbsp tomato purée
2 tsp prepared English mustard
1 small carton (5oz/150g) natural, low-fat yogurt
Salt and black pepper to taste
2 tsp cornflour
1 tbsp chopped parsley to garnish

1.   Skin the kidneys, cut them in half and remove the cores. Place in a saucepan with the stock, mushrooms and tomato purée.
2.   Cook very gently, covered, for 10 minutes or until tender.
3.   Stir in the mustard and yogurt. Season to taste.
4.   Mix the cornflour with a little cold water and stir into the pan. Simmer, stirring, for 2–3 minutes.
5.   Sprinkle with parsley and serve with salad or vegetables from the 'free' list.

TURKEY ROAST WITH PLUM AND APPLE SAUCE

Serves: 4
Calories per portion: 370

Add piles of 'free' vegetables (page 7) for a tasty, midweek treat. If the family wants roast potatoes, cook them the Fatfield way – parboil peeled potatoes, brush with vegetable oil and place under the grill, turning occasionally, until brown. In this way you can have a 2oz (50g) chunk of roast potato for only 55 calories!

1½lb (675g) parsnips, quartered
1 turkey breast roll roast, about 1¼lb (550g)
4 medium cooking apples, peeled, cored and quartered
4 large plums, stoned and chopped (if you use canned
    plums, wash off all the syrup carefully)
2 tsp Hermesetas Sprinkle Sweet
Watercress to garnish

1. Parboil the parsnips in boiling salted water for 3 minutes. Drain well.
2. Spread a large piece of foil over a roasting tin, place the turkey breast on it and surround with the parsnips and half the cooking apples. Seal the foil on top of the meat, and cook in a moderate oven (350°F, 180°C, gas mark 4) for 1½ hours, unwrapping the foil for the last 10 minutes.
3. Meanwhile, make the sauce: cook the rest of the apples and the plums together in a little water for 15 minutes, or until soft. Add the Sprinkle Sweet. Mash or whirl in the blender if you prefer a smoother sauce.
4. Serve the sauce in a warmed jug, and the roast garnished with watercress.

LAMB OR PORK KEBABS

Serves: 4
Calories per serving: About 230

Dish these up with the barbecue sauce below for a midweek treat that's bound to go down well with the whole family. Delicious cherry tomatoes are available at most supermarkets now, and are perfect for kebabs.

1lb (450g) lean, boneless leg of lamb or pork tenderloin
1 large red pepper, cored and deseeded
1 large green pepper, cored and deseeded
4oz (100g) button mushrooms
8oz (225g) cherry tomatoes
A little oil for brushing

1. Cut the meat into cubes, discarding any fat and gristle.
2. Cut the deseeded peppers into squares.
3. Thread the lamb or pork, peppers, mushrooms and tomatoes onto skewers.
4. Brush the vegetables with a little oil.
5. Cook under a preheated grill, turning frequently, until the meat is cooked through and tender.

BARBECUE SAUCE

Serves: 4
Calories per serving: 45

Rich and tangy, this sauce is great with the kebabs above, or with grilled fish, steak or lean chops.

1 clove garlic, crushed
1 small onion, chopped
1 small can (8oz/227g) tomatoes
3 tbsp tomato ketchup
1 tsp French mustard

1 tbsp each bottled brown fruit sauce, Worcestershire
   sauce and soy sauce
1/2 pt (275ml) hot water
1/2 beef stock cube
Seasoning and Hermesetas Sprinkle Sweet to taste

1.   Place the garlic, onion and canned tomatoes in a saucepan. Cook gently until the onion is soft.
2.   Add the ketchup, mustard and sauces.
3.   Dissolve the stock cube in the hot water and add to the saucepan.
4.   Simmer for 5 minutes. Purée in a blender, then season and sweeten to taste.

CHEESE AND CORN BAKE

Serves: 4
Calories per serving: 275

Serve with a crisp green salad.

1lb (450g) potatoes (peeled weight), cooked
1oz (25g) low-fat spread
1 large can (11½oz/326g) sweetcorn, drained
8oz (225g) cottage cheese with chives
4oz (100g) lean unsmoked back bacon, grilled on a rack and chopped
1 tbsp chopped parsley
Salt and black pepper

1.   Boil the potatoes until tender. Drain and mash with the low-fat spread.
2.   Stir the drained sweetcorn, cottage cheese, chopped bacon and parsley into the mashed potato. Season to taste.
3.   Spoon into an ovenproof dish and bake at 400°F, 200°C, gas mark 6 for 20–30 minutes until golden on top.

CHICKEN AND VEGETABLE PIE

Serves: 4
Calories per serving: 380

This basic recipe can be used for fish pie, too. Just leave out the chicken and add cooked, flaked white fish to the vegetables with the peas and seasoning. The calorie count will be slightly lower as white fish has around 25 calories per 1oz (25g), compared with 45 for chicken. If you're really feeling flush, throw in a few prawns (2 calories each) as well.

1 medium onion, chopped finely
2 large carrots, sliced thinly
1lb (450g) chicken breast, skin and fat removed and
    diced
1 can (10.4oz/295g) Weight Watchers from Heinz
    Chicken Noodle Soup
4oz (100g) frozen peas
1 tbsp chopped parsley
2 bay leaves
Salt and black pepper
1½lb (675g) boiling potatoes (peeled weight), cooked and
    mashed with a little skimmed milk
3 slices Weight Watchers from Heinz Reduced Fat
    Processed Cheese, chopped finely
Parsley to garnish

1.   Cook the onion and carrot in a little water until soft. Add the diced chicken and continue cooking until the meat turns white.
2.   Drain off the water, add the soup to the chicken, bring to the boil, cover and simmer gently for 10 minutes.
3.   Add the peas, parsley, bay leaves and seasoning to taste. Cover and simmer gently for 5 minutes. Discard the bay leaves.

4. Meanwhile, prepare the potatoes, then mix two thirds of the chopped cheese with the mashed potato, and season to taste.

5. Put the chicken mixture into a deep ovenproof dish, and fork or pipe the potato on top.

6. Sprinkle with the remaining chopped cheese.

7. Bake at 375°F, 190°C, gas mark 5 for 25–30 minutes. The potato should be browned on top. Garnish with parsley sprigs just before serving.

GAMMON STEAKS WITH PINEAPPLE AND MUSTARD SAUCE

Serves: 4
Calories per serving: 225

This is scrumptious served with a couple of large grilled tomatoes, green beans and a green salad . . . for hardly any extra calories!

4 3oz (75g) lean gammon steaks, fat trimmed off
4 pineapple rings, canned in juice, and drained
1 small carton (5oz/150g) natural, low-fat yogurt
½ tsp made-up English mustard
½ tsp yeast extract
Salt and black pepper
2 tbsp chopped parsley
Parsley sprigs to garnish

1. Place the gammon steaks in a shallow ovenproof dish, and top each one with a pineapple ring.

2. Mix together the remaining ingredients except the parsley garnish, and pour over the ham and pineapple.

3. Cook in a moderate oven (325°F, 170°C, gas mark 3) for 30 minutes. Garnish with parsley sprigs.

LOW CALORIE FISH AND CHIPS

Serves: 4
Calories per serving: 470

You can prepare this meal so quickly that it's hardly worth going to the chippie! What's more, you save about 600 calories!

1½lb (675g) cod or plaice fillets
1 small carton (5oz/150g) natural, low-fat yogurt
4oz (100g) wholemeal breadcrumbs
Salt and black pepper
12oz (350g) oven chips
1 lemon, cut into 4 wedges

1.   Dip the non-skin side of each fillet into the yogurt, then press in seasoned breadcrumbs, coating well.
2.   Lay the fish skinside down on a rack on a flat baking tray and bake in a very hot oven (475°F, 240°C, gas mark 9) for about 20 minutes, or until crisp and golden.
3.   Meanwhile, cook the chips according to the instructions on the packet.
4.   Serve the fish and chips with lemon wedges.

CHAPTER SIX

SPECIAL OCCASION MENUS

Fancy eating gourmet meals with friends and sticking to your diet? You can do it, if *you* do the entertaining! It's easy to take control of your own calorie intake if you are the one who's in the kitchen.

But no one wants to slave over a hot stove all night, so these recipes are simple, as well as impressive and low in calories. Should you tell your guests they are 'slimming' menus? That's up to you, but my advice is to wait until the end of the meal when their tummies are full. They'll never believe you!

Here are the menus in this chapter:

DINNER PARTY FOR SIX

Menu:
    Salmon Pâté with toast triangles
    Chicken Marsala with fluffy rice and crisp green salad
    Ginger fruit salad

Calories per serving:
    Salmon Pâté: *105 (175* with two wholemeal toast triangles)
    Chicken Marsala: *365 (465* with 2 heaped tablespoons of plain, boiled rice)
    Ginger Fruit Salad: *85*

This is a delicious, filling dinner. For your guests, you can add butter to go with the pâté, a cheese course, and thin biscuits to nibble with the fruit salad. The starter and dessert can be made in advance and kept in the fridge until needed.

SALMON PÂTÉ

1 small can (3.7oz/105g) red salmon, drained
4oz (100g) low-fat Cheddar cheese, grated finely
2 tsp lemon juice
2 tsp Worcestershire sauce
2 tbsp reduced-calorie mayonnaise
Grated rind of 1 lemon
1 tbsp finely chopped parsley
1 tbsp chopped nuts
Cucumber and lemon slices to garnish

1.   Beat all the ingredients together.
2.   Chill and serve in small ramekin dishes or on a large platter garnished with cucumber and lemon slices, plus triangles of toast.

CHICKEN MARSALA

6 chicken breasts (8oz/225g each)
Seasoned flour
1 tbsp corn oil
6oz (175g) button mushrooms, sliced
2 tsp flour
5fl oz (150ml) dry white wine
3 tbsp Marsala wine
1 small carton (3½oz/100g) low-fat, natural fromage frais
Salt and black pepper
4oz (100g) Edam cheese, cut into six slices
1oz (25g) flaked almonds, toasted, to garnish
Chopped fresh parsley to garnish

1. Remove the skin and any bones from the chicken breasts and coat in the seasoned flour.
2. Put the oil in a large, heavy-based, non-stick pan, and cook the breasts gently, turning occasionally, for about 15–20 minutes until golden brown and cooked through.
3. Remove from the pan, place in an ovenproof serving dish and keep warm in a low oven.
4. Sauté the mushrooms in the pan, and add to the chicken. Sprinkle the flour in the pan, cook for 1 minute, blending with the bits left in the pan. Gradually add the white wine and Marsala. Bring to the boil, stirring constantly.
5. Add the fromage frais and reheat gently. Do not boil. Season to taste.
6. Poor the sauce over the chicken and place the slices of Edam on top. Brown under a hot grill. Sprinkle with toasted almonds and chopped parsley and serve.

GINGER FRUIT SALAD

1 large Ogen melon
8oz (225g) grapes
8oz (225g) fresh or frozen raspberries
Juice of 1 orange
1 tbs sherry
Pinch of ground ginger
1 small carton (5oz/150g) natural, low-fat yogurt to
    decorate
6 pieces preserved ginger to decorate

1.   Cut the melon in half and remove the seeds. Cut the
flesh into balls with a small teaspoon or use a melon baller
if you have one.
2.   Cut the grapes in half and remove the pips.
3.   Place all the fruit in a bowl.
4.   Mix together the orange juice, sherry and ground
ginger.
5.   Pour over the fruit, place in the fridge and leave to
soak for several hours.
6.   Spoon into small glass dishes and top each with a
spoonful of yogurt and a piece of preserved ginger.

LOVERS' DINNER

Menu:
  Cucumber and Strawberry Salad
  Pork Chops with Rosemary and Orange Sauce
  Fresh Pineapple and Rum Surprise
Calories per serving:
  Cucumber and Strawberry Salad: *25*
  Pork Chops with Rosemary and Orange Sauce: *290*
  Pineapple and Rum Surprise: *120*

If you want to get your partner in the mood for love, give him – or her – this delicious supper. It's light, tasty, low in calories and packed with vitamins and minerals so you'll both feel frisky when you finish the meal! What's more, you can have a couple of glasses of bubbly with your supper and still stick to your diet!

CUCUMBER AND STRAWBERRY SALAD

½ small cucumber, peeled and sliced very thinly
6 strawberries, sliced
1 tbsp dry white wine
Dash of white wine vinegar
Salt and black pepper
Mint sprigs to garnish

1. Arrange the cucumber slices in a heart shape on a large plate.
2. Fill in the centre with the slices of strawberry.
3. Mix together the wine, vinegar and salt and black pepper to taste. Spoon over the salad, cover and chill. Serve garnished with sprigs of mint.

PORK CHOPS WITH ROSEMARY AND ORANGE SAUCE

2 oranges
2 lean pork chops (about 8oz/225g), trimmed of fat
1 tsp dried rosemary
Salt and black pepper

1.   Peel and slice 1 orange and squeeze the juice from the other orange.
2.   Grill the chops until brown on both sides under a medium heat on a rack so any fat drips through and can be discarded. Keep the chops warm on a serving dish.
3.   Meanwhile, heat the orange juice in a small pan with the rosemary. Add the orange slices, and heat through.
4.   Pour the sauce over the chops and serve at once, with a crisp green salad and plenty of 'free' vegetables (*see* page 7).

FRESH PINEAPPLE AND RUM SURPRISE

1 small pineapple
1 dsp Hermesetas Sprinkle Sweet
2 tbsp dark rum
1 kiwi fruit, sliced

1.   Cut the pineapple into quarters, lengthwise, removing the core, but reserving the leaves.
2.   Arrange the quarters attractively on a serving plate.
3.   Mix the Sprinkle Sweet and rum together and pour over the pineapple.
4.   Decorate with sliced kiwi fruit and serve.

CHRISTMAS DINNER FOR EIGHT

Menu:
   Prawn and Grapefruit Cocktail with Seafood Sauce
   Roast Turkey with Prune and Apple Stuffing, Sprouts,
      Green Beans, Bread Sauce, Roast Potatoes and
      Carrots
   Oranges in Grand Marnier

Calories per serving:
   Prawn and Grapefruit Cocktail with Seafood Sauce:
      150
   Roast Turkey with Prune and Apple Stuffing (average
      serving): *360*
   Oranges in Grand Marnier: *120*

There is no doubt that Christmas lunch is the biggest blow-out of the year. It is quite possible to consume 3000 calories at one meal, if you have lashings of stuffing, roast potatoes, pud, cream, chocs, wine and liqueurs. However, if you stick to this basic menu, with a couple of glasses of dry wine, and a small chunk of roast potato and thin gravy you'll stay within 1000 calories. Remember to pile 'free' vegetables like sprouts and green beans on your plate (page 7). My recipe for Turkey Mayonnaise on page 77 is the best one I know for 'recycling' leftover turkey. I usually make a big dish of it for our Boxing Day buffet supper. If you add a crisp salad, and a small baked potato, with fruit to follow, you'll still have change from 450 calories.

PRAWN AND GRAPEFRUIT COCKTAIL WITH SEAFOOD SAUCE

4 pink grapefruit
1lb (450g) peeled prawns
Salad leaves to line the bowls
Sprigs of mint to garnish
Sauce
4 tbsp reduced-calorie mayonnaise
4 tbsp natural, low-fat yogurt
8 tsp tomato ketchup
2–3 drops hot pepper sauce

1.   Peel the grapefruit and remove the pith. Cut between the membranes to remove the segments, and cut each one in half.
2.   Mix the prawns and grapefruit segments together.
3.   Line 8 small bowls with salad leaves and divide the prawn and grapefruit mixture between them.
4.   Mix together the sauce ingredients, adding the hot pepper sauce last – don't add too much. Chill until needed.
5.   Spoon the seafood sauce on top of the prawn and grapefruit cocktail and garnish with sprigs of fresh mint.

ROAST TURKEY WITH PRUNE AND APPLE STUFFING

1 6lb (2.7kg) turkey, fresh or thoroughly defrosted
12oz (350g) fresh breadcrumbs
24 prunes, soaked overnight in water, stoned and
    chopped
4 large apples, cored and chopped
Grated rind and juice of 2 lemons
2 small eggs (size 4), beaten
A little skimmed milk
Salt and black pepper

1.   Mix the breadcrumbs, prunes, pieces of apple and lemon rind. Add the beaten egg and lemon juice to bind the mixture. If necessary add a little milk, depending on how dry you like your stuffing! Season to taste.

2.   Stuff the turkey neck with the mixture, place in a roasting tin with a little water in the bottom and roast in a hot oven (400°F, 200°C, gas mark 6) for about 3 hours, basting frequently.

3.   Serve with green vegetables and carrots (no butter on top, please!), and large chunks of potato roasted the Fatfield way (brush parboiled potatoes with vegetable oil, and brown under the grill).

ORANGES IN GRAND MARNIER

8 oranges
6fl oz (175ml) water
4oz (100g) runny honey
3 tbsp lemon juice
4fl oz (100ml) Grand Marnier

1.   Using a vegetable peeler, peel thin strips of rind from 3 of the oranges.
2.   Peel all the oranges, and remove the white pith. Cut the oranges into round slices and arrange, overlapping, on a serving dish.
3.   In a small saucepan, combine the water and honey. Bring to the boil, add the orange rind and lemon juice. Simmer for 5 minutes. Remove from the heat, and stir in the Grand Marnier.
4.   Pour over the oranges and chill until required.

BOXING DAY TURKEY MAYONNAISE

Serves: 6
Calories per serving: 220

The hint of curry in the sauce satisfies the lust of Christmas guests who are already planning to sneak off to the local Indian restaurant, rather than face yet more cold meat!

1 small onion, chopped
1 clove garlic
4fl oz (100ml) water
1 tbsp tomato purée
½ tsp curry powder
2 tbsp lemon juice
2 tbsp low-sugar apricot jam
4 tbsp reduced-calorie mayonnaise
4 tbsp natural, low-fat yogurt
1lb (450g) cooked, diced turkey
8oz (225g) grapes, green and black
1½oz (40g) flaked almonds
Watercress to garnish

1.   Simmer the onion and garlic in the water with the tomato purée, curry powder and 1 tablespoon of lemon juice for 8 minutes.
2.   Place in a blender with the jam, and blend until smooth. Allow to cool.
3.   In a large bowl, mix the mayonnaise, yogurt and onion mixture. Stir in the diced turkey and chill.
4.   Just before serving, toss the grapes in the remaining tablespoon of lemon juice and stir into the turkey mayonnaise.
5.   Brown the flaked almonds under the grill.
6.   Pile the turkey mixture onto a serving dish, and garnish with the almonds and watercress.

BUFFET PARTY FOR TEN

Menu:
>   Chicken Tandoori with Yogurt and Cucumber
>   Cold Ratatouille
>   Ham and Beansprout Salad
>   Green Salad with Lemon Vinaigrette Dressing
>   Fish Pie with Crunchy Topping
>   Red Fruit Salad
>   Cherry Yogurt Icecream

Calories per serving:
>   Chicken Tandoori with Yogurt and Cucumber: *200*
>   Cold Ratatouille: *35*
>   Ham and Beansprout Salad: *110*
>   Green Salad with Lemon Vinaigrette Dressing: *20*
>   Fish Pie with Crunchy Topping: *235*
>   Red Fruit Salad: *60*
>   Cherry Yogurt Icecream: *115*

The easiest, and cheapest way to cater for a crowd is to serve up a buffet supper. Slimmers usually find that the main pitfalls they face are nibbles like nuts, canapés, and the cheese board.

But with this menu, anyone watching their weight can feel confident that they can eat well and stick to their diet. In fact, you could choose a huge plateful from these goodies for less than 500 calories.

Don't forget to get plenty of soda and sparkling mineral water so your guests can have 'spritzers' instead of straight white wine. It's easy to double, or treble quantities if you are planning a bigger bash.

CHICKEN TANDOORI WITH YOGURT AND CUCUMBER

2 small pieces fresh root ginger, peeled and chopped
4 cloves garlic, peeled and chopped
4 black peppercorns
2 tsp chilli powder
2 tsp ground coriander
1 tsp ground cumin
½ tsp salt
Finely grated rind and juice of 1 lemon
1–2 drops red food colouring
10 chicken breasts, about 6oz (175g) each, skinned
4 small cartons (5oz/150g) natural, low-fat yogurt
Lettuce and tomatoes to garnish
1 cucumber, sliced thinly

1.   Pound the ginger, garlic and peppercorns in a pestle and mortar or use the back of a tablespoon in a small saucepan. Mix with the chilli powder, ground coriander and cumin, salt, lemon rind and juice and red colouring.
2.   Score the chicken 3 times across each breast with a sharp knife, then rub with the tandoori mixture, pressing well into the flesh.
3.   Coat each chicken breast with 1 tablespoon yogurt, and chill for 24 hours.
4.   Cook under a medium grill, turning once, until the chicken is cooked through and the outside is dark red-brown.
5.   Arrange the lettuce and tomato garnish on a large platter and place the chicken on top.
6.   Serve the remaining yogurt separately, with cucumber slices floating on top.

COLD RATATOUILLE

2 large aubergines, sliced
Salt
2 large onions, sliced finely
2 large cans (14oz/397g) tomatoes
2 cloves garlic, peeled and crushed
2 large green or red peppers, cored, deseeded and sliced
    finely
1½lb (675g) courgettes, sliced
1 tsp dried mixed herbs
1 tsp tomato purée
Salt and black pepper

1.   Sprinkle the aubergine slices with salt. Leave to stand for 20 minutes, then rinse with cold water and pat dry with kitchen paper.
2.   Place the onion and aubergine slices in a large, heavy-based, non-stick pan and pour over the tomatoes. Add the garlic and simmer gently for 5 minutes.
3.   Add the peppers and courgettes, stir, cover and simmer for 15 minutes or until the vegetables are cooked but not mushy. Add a little water if necessary.
4.   Stir in the herbs and tomato purée, and simmer for a further 5 minutes.
5.   Remove from the heat, season to taste and pour into a serving dish.
6.   Chill before serving.

HAM AND BEANSPROUT SALAD

8oz (225g) lean ham, cut into strips
1 large cucumber, peeled and cut into 1in (2.5cm) strips
1 small red and 1 small green pepper, cored, deseeded
    and diced finely
1lb (450g) beansprouts, canned or fresh
3 large oranges, peeled, pith removed and cut into
    segments
1 large lettuce, shredded
1 tbsp chopped chives
Dressing
1oz (25g) Danish Blue cheese, crumbled
3oz (75g) Shape Low Fat Soft Cheese
3 tbsp natural, low-fat yogurt

1.　In a large bowl, mix together the ham, cucumber, peppers, beansprouts and orange segments.
2.　Arrange the shredded lettuce in a serving dish, and pile the salad in the centre.
3.　Make the dressing by mixing the Danish Blue cheese with the Soft Cheese and yogurt.
4.　Pour the dressing over the salad and garnish with chopped chives.

GREEN SALAD WITH LEMON VINAIGRETTE DRESSING

1 large lettuce
4oz (100g) spinach, washed and thick stalks removed
1 curly endive
1 cucumber, sliced thinly
12 spring onions, trimmed and chopped finely
4 sticks celery, chopped finely
1 tbsp each chopped tarragon, thyme and parsley to
    garnish

Dressing
4 tbsp wine vinegar
4 tbsp lemon juice
1 tsp Dijon mustard
1 clove garlic, peeled and crushed (optional)
Salt and black pepper

1. Line a salad bowl with lettuce leaves.
2. Shred the remaining lettuce with the spinach and endive, and pile into the bowl.
3. Arrange the cucumber slices on top and scatter over the chopped spring onions and celery.
4. Mix together the dressing ingredients.
5. Scatter the chopped herbs on top of the salad, and toss with the dressing just before serving.

FISH PIE WITH CRUNCHY TOPPING

1lb (450g) carrots, sliced
1lb (450g) leeks, sliced
2 celery hearts, sliced
2lb (900g) boiling potatoes (peeled weight), sliced
1 small carton (5oz/150g), natural, low-fat yogurt
Salt and black pepper
3lb (1.3kg) white fish fillet (e.g. cod, coley)
2 cans (10.4oz/295g) reduced-calorie celery or
    mushroom soup
A little skimmed milk
2lb (900g) tomatoes, sliced
6 tsp Bran Flakes
Parsley sprigs to garnish

1.   Cook the carrots, leeks and celery hearts in boiling water until tender but still crunchy. Drain.
2.   Cook the potatoes until tender, drain and mash with the yogurt. Season to taste.
3.   Simmer the fish in water for 10 minutes. Strain, remove any skin and bones and flake the fish into large chunks.
4.   Pour the soup into a bowl, and blend gently with the fish, carrots, leeks and celery hearts, adding a little skimmed milk if necessary. Adjust the seasoning.
5.   Pile the fish and vegetable mixture into a 3 pint (1.8 litre) pie dish, cover with the tomatoes and spread the mashed potato on top.
6.   Bake in a hot oven (400°F, 200°C, gas mark 6) for 30 minutes, sprinkle on the Bran Flakes and return to the oven for 5 minutes.
7.   Serve garnished with parsley sprigs.

RED FRUIT SALAD

You can, of course, use other red fruits according to what is in season.

4 crisp red apples
2 tbsp lemon juice
8oz (225g) blackberries
8oz (225g) raspberries
8oz (225g) strawberries
8oz (225g) red cherries, stoned
4 large red plums, stoned and chopped
2 tbsp dry sherry
2 tbsp unsweetened apple juice
2 tsp Hermesetas Sprinkle Sweet
Mint leaves to garnish

1. Core and slice the apples, and cover with lemon juice to prevent discolouring.
2. Combine all the fruit in a bowl.
3. Mix together the sherry, apple juice and Sprinkle Sweet.
4. Pour over the fruit, chill, and serve garnished with mint.

CHERRY YOGURT ICECREAM

1 large can (15oz/425g) black cherries, canned in syrup
½pt (275ml) Shape Double
2 small cartons (4½oz/125g) low-calorie Black Cherry
   Yogurt
2 egg whites

1.   Drain the cherries, reserving the syrup, and remove the stones.
2.   Purée the cherries and syrup.
3.   Whip the Double until it holds its shape, and beat in the yogurt and cherry purée.
4.   Whisk the egg whites until stiff, and then fold into the cherry cream.
5.   Place in a large freezerproof container.
6.   Freeze for about 3 hours, then remove and beat before returning to the freezer.
7.   Remove from the freezer about 30 minutes before serving and place in the fridge to soften slightly.

CURRY SUPPER FOR FOUR

Menu:
Cucumber Raita
Quick Keema

Calories per serving:
Cucumber Raita: *45*
Quick Keema: *About 265*

Instead of sending out for a takeaway, save cash (and calories) with a home-cooked curry supper. This simple menu, served with salad and some crisp white wine or lager is ideal for a Friday or Saturday night, when you want to entertain friends without working too hard!

CUCUMBER RAITA

4oz (100g) cucumber, sliced thinly
Salt
2 small cartons (5oz/150g) natural, low-fat yogurt
2oz (50g) spring onions, sliced thinly
1 green chilli, deseeded and chopped finely
Coriander leaves to garnish

1.   Place the cucumber slices in a colander, sprinkle with salt and leave to drain for 30 minutes. Dry thoroughly.
2.   Mix the yogurt with salt to taste and fold in the cucumber, spring onions and chilli.
3.   Place in a serving dish, garnish with coriander leaves and chill until required.

QUICK KEEMA

The Quick Keema is a very easy curry dish which can be prepared in advance and frozen. In fact, many cooks (and I'm one of them) believe that freezing actually improves the flavour of curry. Fatfield slimmer Linda Philpott sometimes adds quartered potatoes and shelled peas to this dish to make it even more substantial.

1lb (450g) lean minced beef
1 medium onion, sliced finely
1 green chilli, deseeded and sliced finely
2 cloves garlic, crushed
Pinch of turmeric
1 tsp each chilli, coriander and cumin powder
1 large can (14oz/397g) tomatoes
4oz (100g) frozen peas
1 tbsp cornflour
1 small carton (5oz/150g) natural, low-fat yogurt

1.   'Dry fry' the minced beef in a large, heavy-based, non-stick saucepan, stirring until the meat changes colour. Drain off all the fat.
2.   Add the onion, chilli, garlic, spices and tomatoes. Cover and cook gently for about 20 minutes.
3.   Add the peas and cook for a further 5 minutes.
4.   Mix the cornflour with a little cold water to make a smooth paste. Stir into the saucepan with the yogurt. Cook, stirring all the time, for 2 minutes, then serve.

KIDS' BUFFET PARTY FOR EIGHT

Menu:
- Wholemeal Pizza Rolls
- Cottage Cheese and Banana Muffins
- Low-Fat Crisps and Vegetable Medley with Three Dips
- Apricot Chiffon Pie

Calories per serving:
- Wholemeal Pizza Rolls: *245*
- Cottage Cheese and Banana Muffins: *190*
- Low-Fat Crisps and Vegetable Medley with Three Dips: *70*
- Apricot Chiffon Pie: *190*

Nowadays, children have sophisticated tastes. They are more likely to go for savoury titbits like crisps and pizza than traditional kiddy favourites like jelly and icecream.

This menu is tasty and cuts back on calories – so mums and dads can tuck in too. More important, it also cuts down fat and provides plenty of fibre. Add fruit 'kebabs' (chunks of fresh or canned fruit such as grapes or pineapple cubes, stuck on skewers), and homemade lemonade or a non-alcoholic punch to drink.

WHOLEMEAL PIZZA ROLLS

8 2oz (50g) soft wholemeal rolls
1 clove garlic
Pinch of salt
2 tsp low-fat spread
4 tbsp tomato purée
16 slices Weight Watchers from Heinz Reduced Fat
     Processed Cheese
1 dsp dried oregano or thyme
8 drained, canned anchovy fillets, sliced
8 stuffed olives, sliced

1. Cut the rolls in half.
2. Crush the garlic with the salt and work into the low-fat spread.
3. Spread both halves of the rolls with the spread and toast under the grill until lightly browned.
4. Spread each half with tomato purée and top each half with 1 cheese slice. Sprinkle lightly with oregano or thyme. Garnish with slices of anchovy and stuffed olives.
5. Just before serving, replace the rolls under the grill until the cheese bubbles.

COTTAGE CHEESE AND BANANA MUFFINS

8 wholemeal muffins
1oz (25g) low-fat spread
A little Marmite
2 bananas
2 tbsp lemon juice
8oz (225g) cottage cheese
1 punnet cress

1. Split the muffins and toast under the grill.
2. Spread with low-fat spread and Marmite.
3. Slice the bananas, and toss in lemon juice to prevent discolouring.
4. Top each muffin half with a spoonful of cottage cheese, a sprinkling of cress and a few banana slices.
5. Replace the tops, and garnish with the rest of the cress.

LOW FAT CRISPS AND VEGETABLE MEDLEY WITH THREE DIPS

2 packets Low-Fat Crisps
Selection of washed and prepared vegetables, cut into
    bite-size pieces – e.g. cucumber, cauliflower, red and
    green peppers, carrot and celery sticks
1 carton (5oz/150g) Shape Onion and Chives Soft Cheese
1 small carton (5oz/150g) natural, low-fat yogurt
2 spring onions, chopped finely
1 tsp lemon juice
1 tsp each ginger and curry powder
$\frac{1}{2}$ tsp paprika
A few drops of Tabasco Sauce
6 tbsp Heidelberg Calorie Reduced Thousand Island
    Dressing
Lemon slices and parsley to garnish

1. Arrange the crisps and vegetables attractively on small plates.
2. To make the cheese and onion dip, mix Shape Onion and Chives Soft Cheese with 1 tablespoon yogurt, 2 spring onions and the lemon juice.
3. To make the curry dip, mix the remaining yogurt with the curry powder, ginger and paprika, and add Tabasco to taste.
4. For the third dip, pour Heidelberg dressing into a small bowl.
5. Place the cheese and curry dips in small bowls and garnish.

APRICOT CHIFFON PIE

4oz (100g) digestive biscuits
2oz (50g) butter
1 large can (15oz/425g) apricots, canned in natural juice
2 tsp powdered gelatine
2 tbsp Hermesetas Sprinkle Sweet
4fl oz (100ml) evaporated milk
1oz (25g) plain or milk chocolate to decorate

1.   Crush the biscuits. Melt the butter and mix with the biscuit crumbs.
2.   Press into an 8in (20cm) flan case and chill until needed.
3.   Drain the apricots and reserve the juice. Place 4 tablespoons of the juice in a small basin and sprinkle the gelatine on the juice. Leave to soak for 5 minutes until spongy. Stand the basin in a pan containing a little simmering water and leave until the gelatine has dissolved.
4.   Purée the apricots with another 4 tablespoons of juice and the Sprinkle Sweet.
5.   Add the dissolved gelatine and stir well.
6.   Whisk the evaporated milk until foamy.
7.   Add the purée and continue to whisk for another minute.
8.   Pour into the flan case, chill, and decorate with grated chocolate when set.

CHAPTER SEVEN

LOW-CALORIE CONTINENTAL CLASSICS

One of the surprising things about foreign travel is watching the locals tucking into calorie-laden meals without putting on weight. Chic French women seem to manage to stay trim on a diet of *pommes frites* and runny cheese, gorgeous Italians can wolf down pasta at every meal without putting on an ounce, and even Spanish waiters stay slinky-hipped on platefuls of paella!

The truth is that most Europeans don't eat their most fattening national dishes every day – and when they do indulge in a high-calorie main course, they invariably follow it with fresh fruit or a simple sorbet.

What's more, even classic Continental cooks are now looking for ways of preparing dishes with fewer fatty ingredients. They're swapping double cream for yogurt or *crème fraîche*, cutting back on butter, and simplifying the rich sauces that used to double or treble the fattening power of fish and meat.

Here's a selection of some of the most popular European dishes, specially for slimmers. They're simple to cook, delicious, and will recapture the magic of those holidays abroad.

FRANCE

COQ-AU-VIN

Serves: 4
Calories per serving: 280

This is a cheapish dinner party dish that looks and tastes really special. Of course, if you are feeling flush, you can upgrade the wine you use – it will make a difference to the price, but won't affect the calories. Serve the coq-au-vin with plain boiled rice and a salad.

4 medium (9oz/250g) chicken leg portions
½ pt (275ml) chicken stock
8oz (225g) button onions, peeled or large onions, peeled and sliced
8oz (225g) button mushrooms
Chopped parsley to garnish
Marinade
2 cloves garlic, crushed (optional)
1 bay leaf
½pt (275ml) red wine
Salt and black pepper

1. Skin the chicken and place in a shallow dish.
2. Mix the marinade ingredients, season to taste, and pour over the chicken. Cover and marinade in the fridge for 3 hours.
3. Remove the chicken from the marinade. Reserve the marinade.
4. Place the chicken in an ovenproof casserole dish, and brown under a hot grill, turning once.
5. Pour the chicken stock over the chicken, add the onions, cover and cook in a moderate oven (350°F, 180°C,

gas mark 4) for about 1½ hours. Add the mushrooms, and cook for a further 20 minutes.

6.   Discard the bay leaf and pour the marinade into a small saucepan. Boil for about 5 minutes to reduce and thicken slightly, then pour over the casserole. Garnish with chopped parsley before serving.

SALAD NIÇOISE

Serves: 4
Calories per serving: 120

4 anchovy fillets
1 clove garlic, cut in half
1lb (450g) new potatoes
1 tbsp oil-free, low-calorie vinaigrette
1 tsp chopped parsley
Salt and black pepper
12 black olives
4 medium, firm tomatoes, quartered
1 small onion, sliced thinly

1.   Wash the anchovy fillets under running water and cut each one into three.
2.   Rub a salad bowl with the cut garlic clove.
3.   Boil and peel the potatoes, slice while still warm and place in the salad bowl. Mix the vinaigrette, parsley and seasoning and pour over the warm potatoes. Toss lightly.
4.   When cool, stir in the olives, anchovy pieces, tomatoes and sliced onion.

MOULES MARINIÈRES

Serves: 2
Calories per serving: 290

Mussels are so easy to prepare and low in calories (about 25 per 1oz/25g shelled weight) that it's surprising that slimmers don't eat them more often. The problem is usually avail- ability, and the fact that it's necessary to eat them the very same day you buy them.

Nowadays, more supermarkets have fresh fish counters with mussels on display. Try them for a treat after a late- night shopping spree. They are incredibly quick to cook, and taste wonderful with bread and a couple of glasses of the cooking wine!

4 pints (2.3 litres) fresh mussels on the shell
2 shallots or 1 medium onion, chopped
4 stalks parsley
1 sprig thyme
Black pepper
¼pt (150ml) dry white wine
¼pt (150ml) water
Chopped parsley to garnish

1. Scrape and clean the mussels in several changes of cold water, discarding any that are not tightly shut.
2. Put the cleaned mussels into a wide pan with the shallots, herbs, freshly ground pepper, wine and water. Cover the pan and cook over a high heat for 5–6 minutes, shaking the pan occasionally. Discard any mussels that do not open.
3. As soon as the mussels open, place them on warm plates.
4. Strain the liquid over the mussels and sprinkle with chopped parsley.

ITALY

FETTUCCINE WITH SMOKED SALMON

Serves: 6 as a starter, 4 as a main course
Calories: 330 or 490

This recipe is often served as a starter in Italian restaurants, smothered in cream! However, it is just as good with natural yogurt and unsweetened fromage frais instead of the cream, and is quite cheap to make if you use smoked salmon 'ends' which you can buy in most supermarkets.

10oz (275g) smoked salmon slices or 'ends'
3 tbsp natural, low-fat yogurt
3 tbsp unsweetened fromage frais, 8 per cent fat
12oz (350g) fettuccine
Black pepper

1.   Cut the salmon into 1in (2.5cm) strips. Mix the yogurt with the fromage frais.
2.   Place the salmon in a bowl, and pour over the yogurt mixture. Leave to stand for about 2 hours.
3.   Cook the pasta in plenty of boiling, salted water until 'al dente' – cooked but still firm with a touch of bite to it.
4.   Heat the salmon mixture in a heavy saucepan over very low heat. Do not allow it to boil.
5.   Pour over the pasta and stir. Season with freshly ground black pepper and serve at once.

SPAGHETTI BOLOGNESE

Serves 4
Calories per serving: 390

It's convenient to use a ready-made sauce for Bolognese, but this can bump up calories alarmingly, once you include the minced beef and the cheese on top.

For instance, a popular commercial red wine and herb sauce 'costs' 350 calories per four servings, compared with under 50 for the homemade kind.

Use the Quick Tomato Sauce recipe on page 114 if you like, or try this version which is closer to the traditional sauce and tastes wonderful. Instead of spaghetti you can also use tagliatelle which is traditionally served in Bologna in northern Italy where this dish originated.

Bolognese Sauce
2oz (50g) lean, unsmoked bacon, chopped finely
1 small onion, chopped finely
8oz (225g) lean minced beef
1 large can (14oz/397g) chopped tomatoes
2oz (50g) carrot, chopped finely
1 stick celery, chopped finely
6 tbsp dry white wine
¼pt (150ml) beef stock or water
Salt and black pepper
Pinch of nutmeg

Pasta
8oz (225g) spaghetti or tagliatelle
1 tbsp grated Parmesan cheese

1.   Dry fry the bacon over a low heat in a heavy based, non-stick pan until it starts to colour.
2.   Add the onion and beef, stirring well to prevent stick-

ing. Continue cooking for a few minutes, then drain off any fat, and transfer the mixture to a large saucepan.

3.   Add the chopped tomatoes, carrot and celery and cook gently for 15 minutes.

4.   Add the wine, stock or water, salt, freshly ground black pepper and a pinch of nutmeg. Stir, cover the saucepan and simmer gently for 30 minutes, stirring occasionally.

5.   Remove from the heat, check the seasoning and serve.

6.   Meanwhile, boil the spaghetti or tagliatelle in plenty of lightly salted water until cooked but 'al dente' or firm with a touch of bite to it. Drain and serve, topped with the sauce and grated Parmesan cheese.

STEAK PIZZAIOLA

Serves: 2
Calories per serving: 350

This recipe makes rump steak taste very special, and is a great choice for a dinner party. Add noodles for your guests, plus a selection of green vegetables from your 'free' list (see page 7).

2 thin rump steaks, about 5oz (150g) each
Salt and black pepper
½ recipe Quick Tomato Sauce (page 114), heated through

1.   Season the steaks with salt and freshly ground black pepper, and place on a rack. Grill on each side under a high heat until cooked.

2.   Transfer to an ovenproof dish, pour the sauce over, and serve.

SPAIN

GAZPACHO

Serves: 4
Calories per serving: 65

This is a perfect summer soup, and so low in calories that you can drink as much as you like. If you prefer a smoother soup put the canned tomatoes in the blender and add the chilled tomato juice afterwards.

1 large cucumber
1 medium green pepper, cored and deseeded
1 medium red pepper, cored and deseeded
3 cloves garlic, chopped
2 tbsp wine vinegar
1½ pts (850ml) tomato juice, chilled
1 small can (8oz/227g) chopped tomatoes, chilled
Juice of ½ a lemon
Salt and black pepper

1.   Cut half the cucumber and peppers into tiny cubes and arrange on a serving dish, as a garnish.
2.   Roughly chop the remaining cucumber and peppers.
3.   Put in a blender with the garlic and wine vinegar. Liquidize until smooth. Stir into the chilled tomato juice.
4.   Finally stir in the chilled chopped tomatoes and lemon juice and season to taste.
5.   Serve in a large bowl, with ice cubes, handing the garnish separately.

SPANISH OMELETTE

Serves: 4
Calories per serving: 275

If you want to make good, low-calorie omelettes, you need a non-stick pan that really is non-stick – i.e. not an old one which has lost most of the non-stick coating. This family-sized version of a Spanish lunchtime favourite includes hardly any oil at all, but has all the taste of the original.

4oz (100g) potato, peeled and diced
2 medium onions, chopped
6 eggs
4oz (100g) lean ham, diced
2oz (50g) frozen peas
2oz (50g) sweetcorn
1 tsp corn oil
Salt and black pepper

1.   Place the diced potato and onion in a saucepan in a little water. Cook gently for about 15 minutes, until the onion is soft and the potatoes are cooked but still firm. Drain.
2.   Break the eggs into a bowl, beat with a fork just enough to blend the yolks and whites thoroughly. Add the potatoes and onion, ham, frozen peas and sweetcorn. Season lightly.
3.   Heat the oil in a large, heavy-based, non-stick pan, pour in the egg mixture and cook until the base is set, about 5 minutes, shaking the pan occasionally to prevent sticking.
4.   Finish cooking the top of the omelette under a high grill, until the top is brown. Serve cut into wedges.

PAELLA VALENCIANA

Serves: 4
Calories per serving: 435

There are many versions of paella, some using both meat and seafood, others with just seafood or vegetables. You can experiment with this basic recipe, adding or subtracting different ingredients.

If you can't afford the prawns and mussels, it's almost as tasty with chunks of tuna (canned in brine) and chopped, grilled low-fat sausage instead.

The main rule to follow is that the liquid should be double the volume of the rice, and allow about 2oz (50g) of rice for each person.

2 tsp vegetable oil
3 cloves garlic, chopped (optional)
1 medium onion, chopped
3 medium tomatoes, blanched, peeled and chopped or 1
    small can (8oz/227g) tomatoes
1 medium red pepper, cored, deseeded and sliced
4 chicken drumsticks
1 tsp paprika
8oz (225g) long grain white rice
½ tsp yellow food colouring or turmeric
1pt (575ml) chicken stock, seasoned
8oz (225g) frozen peas
8oz (225g) cooked, shelled shrimps or prawns
1pt (575ml) mussels, scrubbed and bearded
Lemon wedges and parsley sprigs to garnish

1.   Heat the oil in a large, deep, heavy-based, non-stick frying pan. Add the garlic, onion, tomatoes, red pepper and chicken pieces. Reduce the heat and add the paprika.

2.   Cook for 10 minutes, stirring occasionally to prevent sticking.

3.   Spread the rice evenly in the pan and stir briefly.

4.   Remove the pan from heat and add the food colouring or turmeric and the stock.

5.   Return to the heat, bring to the boil and add the peas. Cover with a lid or foil.

6.   Simmer gently over a low heat for 15 minutes, or until the rice has cooked and almost all of the stock has been absorbed. Add the shrimps or prawns. If necessary, add a little extra water to prevent the rice sticking while cooking.

7.   Put the mussels on top of the rice, cover and cook for about 5 minutes or until the mussels open. Discard any that remain shut.

8.   Serve the paella hot, garnished with lemon wedges and parsley sprigs.

PORTUGAL

CALDO VERDE

Serves: 4
Calories per serving: 120

This soup is served as a starter in many Portuguese homes. It is an unusual way of serving good old cabbage and spuds, and is very tasty and filling. Recommended for lunch, with a crusty roll and fruit to follow.

2 pts (1.3 litres) water
4 medium potatoes, peeled and sliced
½ small cabbage, with coarse veins and leaves removed, shredded finely
Salt and black pepper
4 tbsp natural, low-fat yogurt
Paprika and a little chopped parsley to garnish

1.   Bring the water to the boil in a large saucepan, add the potatoes and salt to taste. Cover, reduce the heat and cook the potatoes until tender.
2.   Remove the potatoes, mash, return them to the pan and stir to mix.
3.   Add the shredded cabbage, bring the mixture to the boil, and cook for 5 minutes. Season to taste.
4.   Pour into four warmed soup bowls, add a spoonful of yogurt to each one, and sprinkle with paprika and chopped parsley.

PORTUGUESE COD

Serves: 4
Calories per serving: 280

1½lb (675g) cod fillet
1 large can (14oz/397g) chopped tomatoes
1 glass dry white wine
1 large onion, chopped finely
4oz (100g) long grain white rice
1 clove garlic, crushed
Parsley sprigs and lemon slices to garnish

1.   Place the tomatoes and wine in a saucepan, add the chopped onion, rice and garlic. Cover and cook gently until the rice is tender, about 15 minutes.
2.   Meanwhile, cut the fish into 4 cutlets and poach in a little water until cooked through but still firm. Drain and keep warm.
3.   Place the fish in a warmed serving dish, surround with the tomato and rice mixture, and garnish with parsley and lemon slices.

<u>GREECE</u>

BAKED STUFFED AUBERGINES

Serves: 4
Calories per serving: 80

Aubergines absorb oil very quickly indeed, which is why this Greek speciality is usually taboo for slimmers. For example, a 1oz (25g) aubergine slice contains just 4 calories, but fried in oil or fat, this figure zooms up to 60! Our version cuts out the oil completely, and is still yummy hot or cold.

2 large aubergines
2 tsp salt
1/4pt (150ml) chicken stock
1 medium onion, chopped
1 clove garlic, crushed
3 tomatoes, skinned and chopped
1 tbsp chopped chives
1 tbsp sweetcorn
Salt and black pepper
1oz (25g) wholemeal breadcrumbs
1oz (25g) Edam cheese, grated

1.   Cut the aubergines in half lengthwise, slash the flesh and sprinkle with salt. Place, flat side down, on a plate and leave to drain for 1 hour. Rinse thoroughly, and pat dry with kitchen paper, then remove and chop the flesh, leaving the skins whole.
2.   Put 2 tablespoons of the stock into a non-stick pan, cover and cook the onion and garlic gently until soft. Add the aubergine flesh, tomatoes, chives, sweetcorn and seasoning to taste. Cook until the vegetables are soft, then pile into the aubergine cases.

3.   Place the aubergines in a shallow ovenproof dish. Mix together the breadcrumbs and cheese and sprinkle over the aubergines.

4.   Add the remaining stock to the dish, and cover with foil.

5.   Bake in a moderate oven (375°F, 190°C, gas mark 5) for 30 minutes. Serve hot or cold.

HUMMUS

Serves: 6
Calories per serving: 120

This is a simple-to-make starter which is delicious with pitta bread or crispbreads. Usually, the recipe includes olive oil, but this version tastes just as good and saves around 300 calories!

2 large cans (14oz/397g) chick peas
2 cloves garlic, crushed
2 tbsp lemon juice
1 tbsp sesame seeds
Salt and black pepper
Paprika and lemon slices to garnish

1.   Drain the chick peas, reserving the liquid, and put into a food processor or blender with 4fl oz (100ml) of the liquid.

2.   Add the garlic, lemon juice and sesame seeds.

3.   Blend until smooth and season to taste with salt and freshly ground black pepper.

4.   Garnish with paprika and lemon slices.

CHAPTER EIGHT

MICRO MAGIC

Microwave ovens are great for slimmers. Food can be cooked fast, without added fat, and imaginative dishes prepared in less time than it takes to raid the biscuit tin. You can defrost low-calorie meals like soups and casseroles rapidly, saving time and money.

For people who live alone or are alone at home during the day, micros are absolutely slimsational. While it seems time-consuming and wasteful to use a conventional oven to cook something for one person, it is quick, easy and economical to use the microwave. 'Instant' meals like baked potatoes topped with baked beans or cottage cheese, fresh fish with vegetables, nourishing thick soups are all filling and low in calories when cooked the micro way. You also save on washing up, because many meals can be eaten from the same dishes they are cooked in.

There are, of course, certain rules that must be followed by micro fans. It is vital to check that the food is cooked properly, particularly if it has been defrosted before cooking. Soups and casseroles should be stirred halfway through. Reheat food rapidly and thoroughly. Don't keep reheating it, you'll destroy vitamins and minerals. A ready-prepared dish being reheated should register at least 65°C (150°F), after you remove it from the micro. After standing time (during which the food carries on cooking), the temperature should rise by a few degrees. If in doubt, use a micro thermometer to check.

Covering food helps retain moisture, speeds up cooking

and prevents splatters in the oven. Cling film is often used to retain moisture on vegetables and casseroles, but you can use kitchen paper or paper napkins to cover baked potatoes – paper is porous and lets the steam escape. Don't forget to prick items like potatoes and low-fat sausages to prevent explosions!

These recipes are very simple and quick. They have been tried out by busy slimmers using a 650-watt microwave oven with a turntable. If your cooker is a higher wattage, decrease the cooking time slightly, and if it is lower, increase it. If it doesn't have a turntable, turn the dish once or twice during cooking.

INSTANT BREAKFAST

Serves: 1
Calories per serving: 220

Who says slimmers have to leap out of bed at dawn to cook breakfast? In just 2 minutes you can serve up this substantial high-fibre meal. Just add a glass of unsweetened orange juice and you'll be set up for the day. What's more, your diet won't be sabotaged by an attack of the mid-morning munchies!

1 slice wholemeal toast
1 small can (5.29oz/150g) baked beans
3 small tomatoes, halved
1 tbsp sweetcorn

1. Place the toast on a plate and pour the baked beans on top.
2. Arrange the tomatoes and sweetcorn around the toast.
3. Cook on High for 2 minutes.

PEARS WITH GINGER AND CHEESE STUFFING

Serves: 2
Calories per serving: 120

The combination of these three flavours is unusual, and delicious. Serve this for dessert, or for breakfast when you fancy a treat!

2 ginger biscuits
2oz (50g) skimmed milk soft cheese
2 medium pears, peeled, halved and cored
2 tbsp unsweetened apple juice

1. Crush the biscuits and mix with the cheese.
2. Place the pear halves in a serving dish, hollow side up. Fill with the ginger and cheese mixture. Pour the apple juice around the pears.
3. Cover with cling film, pierce and microwave on High for 1½–2 minutes.

HOT SPICED GRAPEFRUIT

Serves: 2
Calories per serving: 15

This makes a change from the usual cold grapefruit starters. Serve it for Sunday brunch (with Boston Baked Beans, page 40, to follow), or before a rich-tasting main course at a dinner party.

1 grapefruit
1 tbsp Less Sharp PLJ Lemon Juice
1 tsp ground nutmeg
1 tsp ground cinnamon
Orange slices to garnish

1. Halve the grapefruit, and loosen the segments with a grapefruit knife.
2. Sprinkle with the PLJ and spices.
3. Place in 2 individual dishes, and cook on High for 2 minutes. Serve hot, garnished with orange slices.

MICRO CHIPS

Serves: 4
Calories per serving: 115

Just for a change, try making your own chips. It's very quick indeed in a micro, and they are guaranteed to be lovely and fresh! Get your grill very hot for the final browning. If you want posher, sauté potatoes, simply cut them into slices instead of chips and garnish with chopped parsley.

1lb (450g) potatoes, peeled weight
1 tbsp vegetable oil
Salt to taste

1. Peel, rinse and dry the potatoes, and cut into ½in (1cm) chips.
2. Place in an ovenproof dish, cover with kitchen paper and cook on High for 4 minutes. Stir and cook for a further 3 minutes.
3. Drain, pat dry with kitchen paper and brush with oil. Sprinkle with salt.
4. Brown the chips under a hot, preheated grill, turning to ensure even browning.

ITALIAN CAULIFLOWER

Serves: 4
Calories per serving: 110

This recipe has a delicious sauce which we have pared down to the minimum calorie count possible without sacrificing the taste. Add some noodles (no butter – you don't need it), if you're serving this as a supper dish and it's good on its own for lunch. Two greedy slimmers could share this and still get away with a 220-calorie lunchtime total!

1 large cauliflower
4 tbsp water
1 medium onion, chopped finely
1 large can (14oz/397g) tomatoes
4 stuffed olives, sliced
Pinch of marjoram
1 clove garlic, crushed (optional)
1 can (10.4oz/295g) low-calorie Chicken Soup
3 tbsp natural, low-fat yogurt
2oz (50g) low-fat Cheddar cheese, grated

1.   Wash the cauliflower and remove the outer green leaves. Break into large florets.
2.   Place in a large dish with the water, cover with perforated cling film and cook for 10 minutes on High. Move the florets around halfway through cooking.
3.   Place the onion in a bowl with 3 tablespoons of juice from the tomatoes. Cover and cook on High for 3 minutes.
4.   Add the olives, tomatoes, marjoram and garlic. Cover and cook on High for 2 minutes, stirring after 1 minute.
5.   Stir and pour over the cauliflower.
6.   Combine the soup and yogurt, pour over the cauliflower, sprinkle with cheese and cook on High for 2 minutes.

TEN-MINUTE CHILLI

Serves: 4
Calories per serving: 290

This is a warming treat on cold winter nights. Serve it, piping hot, in individual bowls with crusty bread or plain boiled rice and a crisp salad.

1 onion, chopped finely
1 green pepper, cored, deseeded and diced
12oz (350g) lean, minced beef
1 large can (15oz/425g) red kidney beans
4 tbsp liquid from the can
4 tbsp tomato purée
1 tsp chilli powder
½ tsp ground cumin
Salt and black pepper
Chopped parsley and cucumber slices

1. Put the onion and green pepper into a 2pt (1.2 litre) casserole, cover and cook on High for 4 minutes to soften.
2. Add the beef, bean liquid, tomato purée and chilli powder or cumin to taste. Stir thoroughly, cover with cling film, perforate and cook on High for 5 minutes.
3. Remove from the oven, remove the cling film and stir. Cover again and cook for a further 3 minutes.
4. Add the beans and stir well. Cook on High for 2 minutes.
5. Season to taste with salt and freshly ground black pepper and serve garnished with parsley and cucumber slices.

QUICK TOMATO SAUCE

Serves: 6
Calories per serving: 20

You can make this up in larger quantities and keep it in the freezer until needed. I use it as a base for scrumptious low-calorie toppings for pasta (adding prawns, cooked chopped chicken, etc.) or with lean minced beef (dry-fried and drained of fat). I also like to toss finely chopped vegetables (e.g. courgettes, green beans or cauliflower) into a saucepan full of the sauce, to make a delicious lunchtime soup. The garlic is optional!

1 small onion, chopped finely
¼pt (150ml) chicken stock
1 large can (14oz/397g) chopped tomatoes
2 cloves garlic, crushed (optional)
Salt and black pepper
Pinch of marjoram
1 tbsp tomato purée
1 tsp cornflour

1. Place the onion in a bowl with 3 tablespoons of stock. Cook on High for 2 minutes.
2. Add the remaining ingredients, except the tomato purée and cornflour.
3. Stir well, cover with perforated cling film, and cook for 5 minutes on High.
4. Remove the cling film, add the tomato purée to the sauce, and the cornflour mixed with a little water. Stir well.
5. Continue cooking for another 5 minutes, stirring once every minute.
6. If you like a smoother sauce, you can whizz it through the food blender before serving.

SCAMPI WITH WHITE WINE AND TOMATO SAUCE

Serves: 4
Calories per serving: 220

This has to be the quickest-ever dinner party dish. If scampi are too expensive, the sauce is equally scrumptious with any firm white fish.

1½lb (750g) frozen uncooked scampi, defrosted
1 small glass dry white wine
1 large onion, chopped finely
2 cloves garlic, crushed
½ small red pepper, cored, deseeded and cubed
2 tbsp tomato purée
2 tbsp chopped fresh basil or parsley
Salt and black pepper

1.   Place the scampi on a shallow dish, keeping the pieces separate. Pour over the white wine. Cook on High for 2 minutes, stirring after 1 minute.
2.   Transfer the scampi to another dish. Put the onion, garlic and red pepper into the dish containing the wine, and cook on High for 5 minutes.
3.   Add the tomato purée and most of the basil or parsley. Cover with cling film, pierce and cook on High for 5 minutes, stirring once. Season to taste.
4.   Add the scampi, cover and cook on High for 3 minutes. Garnish with the remaining basil or parsley.

COD STEAK ORIENTAL

Serves: 1
Calories per portion: 210

This is scrumptious enough for a dinner party, served with bean sprouts, fluffy rice and salad. Yet, it can be whizzed up in only 4 minutes. You can use the sauce with any white fish, or even with a chicken breast.

8oz (225g) cod fillet, defrosted
1 tsp lemon juice
1 tsp soy sauce
1 tsp tomato juice
Pinch of ground ginger
Salt to taste
1 small orange to garnish
Watercress to garnish

1.   Place the cod on a plate or serving dish.
2.   Combine the lemon juice, soy sauce, tomato juice and a pinch of ground ginger. Add a little salt to taste.
3.   Pour over the fish.
4.   Cover and cook on High for 3 minutes or until the fish is cooked.
5.   Slice the orange.
6.   Remove the fish from the oven, allow to stand, then garnish with orange slices and watercress.

TUNA-STUFFED TOMATOES

Serves: 1
Calories per serving: 150

I love cooking stuffed tomatoes in a micro. It takes just minutes to dish up something that's really tasty and special. In this recipe, I've used tuna as stuffing, but you could also use chopped leftover chicken with brown rice and onion, or wholemeal breadcrumbs with herbs, garlic and a little stock. Serve with plenty of 'free' salad vegetables (see page 7).

One of my other favourite low-calorie tomato tricks is to micro leftover tomato salad (seasoned with lemon juice, wine vinegar and herbs), and throw it on top of a couple of slices of toast. With lashings of Worcestershire sauce and a dollop of cottage cheese, this is a gorgeous breakfast or lunchtime treat for less than 250 calories.

2 large tomatoes
1 small can (3½oz/99g) tuna in brine, drained and
    mashed
½oz (15g) onion, chopped finely
Pinch each of celery salt and dried or chopped fresh
    parsley

1. Slice the tops off the tomatoes, scoop out the pulp and mix with the remaining ingredients.
2. Fill the tomatoes, replace the tops and cook on High for 3 minutes.

BAKED POTATO WITH CHEESE AND PRAWNS

Serves: 1
Calories per serving: 275

This is a luxury version of one of our favourite Fatfield lunches. Add masses of salad and vegetables from your 'free' list for a great meal (see page 7). Even if you throw in a glass of dry wine, the calorie total is still under 400, less than a boring old cheese sandwich!

1 8oz (225g) potato, washed, dried and pricked
1oz (25g) red pepper, chopped
2oz (50g) cottage cheese with chives and onion
1½oz (40g) peeled prawns
Chopped parsley to garnish

1. Place the potato on kitchen paper and cover with another piece of paper.
2. Microwave on High for 4 minutes.
3. Turn over and cook for a further 4 minutes. Check that it is cooked through. Leave to stand while preparing the filling.
4. Mix the pepper with the cottage cheese and prawns.
5. Split the top of the potato and pile on the filling.
6. Garnish with chopped parsley and serve with 'free' vegetables.

SUMMER PUDDING

Serves: 6
Calories per serving: 95

You can use fresh or frozen fruit for this traditional recipe, which is actually delicious at any time of the year. Serve it with natural, low-fat yogurt or unsweetened fromage frais.

1½lb (750g) mixed summer fruits (raspberries, blackcurrants, blackberries, redcurrants, cherries, strawberries), fresh or frozen
4fl oz (100ml) unsweetened apple juice
Hermesetas Sprinkle Sweet to taste
5oz (150g) sliced white bread, crusts removed

1.   If fresh fruit is used, place in a large bowl with the apple juice. Cover and microwave on High for 4–6 minutes or until lightly cooked, stirring halfway through the cooking time.
2.   If using frozen fruit, place it in a large bowl, cover and microwave on Defrost for 8–9 minutes, stirring halfway through the cooking time. Microwave on High for 2 minutes. Stir in the apple juice.
3.   Leave the fruit to cool and then add Sprinkle Sweet to taste.
4.   Line a 1½pt (850ml) pudding basin with some of the bread.
5.   Fill with half of the fruit. Cover with a slice of bread, then top with the remaining fruit.
6.   Completely cover the top with the rest of the bread.
7.   Place a saucer on top, and weight down with a can of food.
9.   Chill for 8 hours or overnight.
9.   Turn out the pudding onto a plate to serve.

BAKED APPLE WITH RUM

Serves: 1
Calories per serving: 110

This is just about the lowest-calorie hot dessert you can serve, and it is absolutely delicious. You could add cider or calvados instead of the rum without adding too many extra calories. My assistant, Toni, adds $1/2$oz (15g) sultanas and a dribble of honey which increases the calorie count to 130. You can add rice pud or semolina for the children.

1 medium cooking apple, cored
1 tbsp water mixed with 1 tbsp Hermesetas Sprinkle
    Sweet to taste

1.   Slit the skin around the middle of the apple, and place it in a serving dish. Pour over the liquid.
2.   Cook on High for 2–3 minutes, or until cooked but not mushy.

CHAPTER NINE

VEGGIE SLIMSATIONS

If you're green, it's easy to be lean! Not strictly true, I'm afraid, as many vegetarians find that they put on weight once they give up meat. Reasons? It's so tempting to fill up that space on your plate with calorie-loaded foods like cheese, quiches, nuts and creamy pasta dishes. Even vegans, who give up all animal products, sometimes get hooked on high-calorie nibbles and snacks.

But, if you are careful with calories, a veggie diet can be a Fatfield diet, too. Many vegetables can be eaten freely on the diet (check out the list on page 7), so all you have to do is prepare them imaginatively.

Invest in some large, flattish casseroles for cooking superb meals in the oven. Make up tasty vegetable sauces to go with pasta (which contains just 30 calories per 1oz/25g), cooked weight, until you pile cheese and cream on top!) and keep a look out for unusual vegetables like salsify, celeriac, and seakale.

Pulses, such as haricot beans, kidney beans and chick peas, should be kept in every vegetarian store cupboard. Another useful ingredient is Quorn, which is a new food, harvested from a tiny, mushroom-like plant. It is high in fibre and protein, contains no fat or cholesterol and is relatively low in calories.

These recipes will appeal to vegetarians and non-vegetarians alike, but they are not all suitable for vegans.

CHEESE AND VEGETABLE STIR-FRY

Serves: 4
Calories per serving: 160

1lb (450g) mixed crisp vegetables such as carrots, leeks,
    courgettes, sweet peppers, green beans, cauliflower
    and broccoli
1 tbsp sunflower oil
½ tsp each ground cumin, coriander and garam masala
Finely grated rind and juice of 1 large orange
4oz (100g) Edam cheese, cut into ½in (1cm) cubes
4 spring onions, cut into curls to garnish

1.   Wash and dry the vegetables and cut into pieces –
slice leeks, courgettes, carrots and peppers and break
cauliflower and broccoli into florets.
2.   Heat the oil in a heavy-based, non-stick pan over a
medium heat. Add the vegetables and spices and stir-fry
for 2 minutes.
3.   Add the orange rind and juice, bring to the boil, then
reduce the heat and simmer for 3–4 minutes until the
vegetables are just tender.
4.   Add the cheese cubes and stir for a few seconds until
heated through, and the cheese is beginning to melt.
5.   Serve immediately, garnished with spring onion curls.

FRUITY QUORN CURRY

Serves: 3
Calories per serving: 150

Add 4 tablespoons plain, boiled rice and a cool, delicious salad of cucumber with natural, low-fat yogurt and chopped fresh mint, and you'll still consume less than 250 calories! So, who needs a greasy takeaway?

1 tbsp mild curry paste
2 tbsp apricot chutney
1 small can (8oz/227g) chopped tomatoes
1 tbsp sultanas
3 tbsp water
4½ oz (125g) Quorn pieces
1 medium onion, sliced
1 small yellow pepper, cored, deseeded and sliced
1 medium carrot, cut into julienne strips
2oz (50g) mushrooms, sliced
1 stick celery, chopped
1 medium red apple, cored and roughly chopped

1.   Mix the curry paste, chutney, tomatoes, sultanas and water in a large pan. Cook, stirring, for 2 minutes.
2.   Add the Quorn and onion, cover and simmer for 5 minutes to allow the Quorn to absorb the flavour of the sauce.
3.   Add the pepper and carrot and cook for 5 minutes.
4.   Add the mushrooms and cook for 1 minute.
5.   Add the celery and red apple and heat through.

STUFFED MARROW WITH TOMATO SAUCE

Serves: 4
Calories per serving: 200

1 medium marrow
1oz (25g) grated nuts
4oz (100g) wholemeal breadcrumbs
¼pt (150ml) skimmed milk
Mixed herbs and salt to taste
1 egg
1 small onion, chopped finely
1oz (25g) low-fat spread
½ tsp yeast extract
1oz (25g) low-fat Cheddar cheese, grated
Sauce
1 large can (14oz/397g) chopped tomatoes
1 small onion, chopped finely
1 clove garlic, chopped finely (optional)
1 tsp dried thyme

1.   Wash and scrub the marrow, and cut in half length-wise.
2.   Scoop out the seeds and pith and discard.
3.   Mix together the nuts, breadcrumbs, milk, herbs, salt and egg in a small bowl.
4.   Soften the chopped onion in a little low-fat spread in a saucepan.
5.   Add the stuffing mixture and yeast extract and cook for another minute.
6.   In a large pan, boil the marrow halves for about 5 minutes. Drain.
7.   Place the marrow halves in an ovenproof dish, fill with the stuffing mixture and top with the grated cheese and remaining low-fat spread.

8.   Bake in a moderate oven (325°F, 170°C, gas mark 3) for about 30 minutes or until the marrow is tender. Test with the tip of a pointed knife.

9.   While the marrow is cooking, mix the sauce ingredients in a small saucepan, cover and cook gently for about 20 minutes.

10.   To serve cut each marrow piece in half and pour the sauce on top.

LEEK PIE

Serves: 4
Calories per serving: 160

1lb (450g) leeks, trimmed, washed thoroughly and cut
   into ½in (1cm) slices
1 small carton (5oz/150g) Shape Low Fat Soft Cheese
1lb (450g) potatoes (peeled weight), cooked and mashed
   with ¼pt (150ml) skimmed milk

1.   Boil the leeks in water until cooked but still crisp. Drain thoroughly.

2.   Place the leeks in a shallow, ovenproof dish and mix in the Shape Soft Cheese.

3.   Pile the mashed potato on top, covering the leeks and cheese. Use a fork to decorate the top.

4.   Bake in a moderate oven (375°F, 190°C, gas mark 5) for 25–30 minutes. Flash under the grill just before serving to brown the top.

MIXED VEGETABLE CASSEROLE

Serves: 4
Calories per serving: 60

Non-veggies can serve this delicious casserole with a roast chicken leg, no skin, and still have 'change' out of 350 calories. It is also a super lunch dish, with crusty bread for dunking!

1 tsp low-fat spread
8oz (225g) swede, sliced
2 carrots, sliced
1 large onion, sliced
2 sticks celery, chopped
2 medium leeks, sliced
Salt and black pepper
Pinch of nutmeg
1 large can (14oz/397g) tomatoes
2 tbsp natural, low-fat yogurt
Chopped parsley to garnish

1.   Lightly grease a 3 pint (1.8 litre) casserole with the low-fat spread.
2.   Arrange the vegetables in the dish in layers, sprinkling each layer with seasoning and a pinch of nutmeg.
3.   Pour the tomatoes over the vegetables, cover and cook in a moderate oven (350°F, 180°C, gas mark 4) for about 1 hour, or until the vegetables are tender.
4.   Just before serving, remove the lid, swirl yogurt on top of the tomatoes and sprinkle with chopped parsley.

BRAISED RED CABBAGE WITH APPLE CHEESE

Serves: 2
Calories per serving: 110

This is a favourite dish of successful Fatfield slimmer Linda Philpott, who says it is scrumptious for lunch with a small baked potato and lots of green salad.

1lb (450g) red cabbage, shredded
4oz (100g) cooking apple, cored, peeled and sliced
4oz (100g) onion, sliced
1oz (25g) brown sugar
2 tbsp wine vinegar
4 tbsp water
2oz (50g) Shape Low Fat Soft Cheese
1 cooking apple, cooked and puréed
Salt and black pepper

1.   Place the cabbage, apple slices, onion, sugar, vinegar and water in a saucepan. Cover and simmer for 20–30 minutes, until the cabbage is nearly soft.
2.   Blend the soft cheese and the apple purée together and stir into the cabbage. Season to taste.

COURGETTES WITH HARICOT BEANS

Serves: 4
Calories per serving: 170

Add 3 tablespoons plain boiled rice, and a leafy green salad for a substantial supper dish that's under 290 calories. Yummy!

6oz (175g) haricot beans, soaked in water overnight
1 large can (14oz/397g) chopped tomatoes
1 green pepper, cored, deseeded and sliced
1 onion, sliced
1 clove garlic, crushed
1lb (450g) courgettes, sliced thickly
2 tsp dried basil
1 small carton (5oz/150g) natural, low-fat yogurt

1.   Drain the beans, cover with fresh water and boil for about 45 minutes, or until tender.
2.   Pour the tomatoes into a large saucepan, add the green pepper, onion, garlic, courgettes and basil, cover and simmer for about 15 minutes, until the vegetables are almost cooked.
3.   Stir in the drained beans, heat through, transfer to a serving dish, and pour the yogurt on top.

FATFIELD PAN HAGERTY

Serves: 4
Calories per serving: 280

The traditional Geordie dish, Pan Hagerty, is usually cooked in a frying pan with lashings of fat. But this version, developed by the Fatfield villagers, is just as delicious, and very filling.

1 tsp low-fat spread
2lb (900g) potatoes (peeled weight), cut into thin slices
1lb (450g) onions, sliced
3oz (75g) low-fat Cheddar cheese, grated
1 carton (5oz/150g) natural, low-fat yogurt
Salt and black pepper

1.   Grease a large, shallow ovenproof dish with the low-fat spread.
2.   Place layers of the potatoes, onions, and grated cheese in the dish, ending with a layer of cheese.
3.   Pour the yogurt evenly over the top, cover loosely with foil and place in a moderate oven (350°F, 180°C, gas mark 4) for 1 hour or until the vegetables are tender.
4.   Remove the foil, and brown the top of the dish under a high grill for a few moments until golden.

SWEET AND SOUR TOFU

Serves: 4
Calories per serving: 385

4oz (100g) long grain brown rice
1lb (450g) tofu, cut into small cubes
1 small bunch spring onions, chopped finely
1 dsp corn oil
1 large can (14oz/397g) tomatoes
1 medium can (15oz/425g) pineapple chunks, canned in
    juice
2oz (50g) whole almonds
4 tbsp soy sauce

1.   Cook the brown rice in plenty of boiling water until still 'nutty' but tender.
2.   In a heavy-based, non-stick pan, fry the tofu and spring onions in the oil very gently for about 3 minutes.
3.   Add the tomatoes, drained pineapple, almonds and soy sauce.
4.   Simmer gently for 5 minutes.
5.   Serve poured over the cooked rice.

ONIONS STUFFED WITH BAKED BEANS

Serves: 2
Calories per serving: 250

4 large onions
1 medium can (7.9oz/225g) curried beans with sultanas
2 tbsp mango chutney, chopped
1 large tomato, chopped
1 tsp low-fat spread for greasing dish (make it less, if
    you can!)
2 tbsp water

1.   Put the peeled onions in a large pan and cover with
cold water. Bring to the boil, cover and simmer for about
35 minutes, or until tender but still firm. Test with the tip
of a pointed knife.
2.   Drain, leave to cool, then cut a small slice from the
base of each onion so it stands firmly.
3.   Remove the centre of each onion with a small spoon,
chop finely and place in a bowl.
4.   Mix the chopped onion with the beans, chutney and
chopped tomato.
5.   Stand the onions in a greased ovenproof dish, pile the
bean stuffing back into the onions, and add the water to the
dish.
6.   Cover and cook for 25 minutes in a hot oven (400°F,
200°C, gas mark 6).

COURGETTES AU GRATIN

Serves: 4
Calories per serving: 230

You can use broccoli, shredded cabbage or leeks instead of courgettes for this dish. Serve it with crusty bread and a crisp green salad.

1 large onion, sliced into rings
1 large can (14oz/397g) chopped tomatoes
2lb (900g) courgettes, sliced into ½in (1cm) pieces
Salt and black pepper
1 tsp dried oregano
8oz (225g) Edam cheese, grated
Chopped parsley to garnish

1.   Place the onion rings and tomatoes in a large, shallow, non-stick saucepan.
2.   Cook gently over a medium heat until the onion is softened.
3.   Add the courgettes and continue cooking for 10 minutes, turning the vegetables to prevent sticking.
4.   Season with salt, freshly ground black pepper and oregano. Stir thoroughly.
5.   Place in a shallow, ovenproof dish and sprinkle with the cheese.
6.   Cover with foil and bake in a moderate oven (375°F, 190°C, gas mark 5) for 20 minutes. Serve sprinkled with chopped parsley.

LENTIL KEDGEREE

Serves: 4–6
Calories per serving: 435 or 290

This can either be served alone as a substantial supper dish for 4 people, or with grilled vegeburgers, in which case there is enough for 6.

12oz (350g) whole brown lentils, soaked and drained
6oz (175g) brown long grain rice
2 tsp curry powder
1 tbsp chopped parsley
Salt and black pepper
1 small onion, sliced thinly
1 red pepper, cored, deseeded and sliced thinly
1 hard-boiled egg, quartered

1. Cook the lentils in boiling, unsalted water for about 25 minutes, or until tender. Drain.
2. Meanwhile, cook the rice in boiling, salted water for 30 minutes, or until tender but still 'nutty'. Drain and stir in the curry powder.
3. Mix together the cooked lentils and rice, stir in most of the parsley, and season to taste.
4. Pour the mixture into a heated serving dish, and garnish with onion and pepper rings, hard-boiled egg quarters and the rest of the parsley.

BANANA AND NUT SALAD

Serves: 4
Calories per serving: 335

4 medium bananas, sliced
1 large red apple, cored and chopped
2 tbsp lemon juice
4oz (100g) long grain brown rice (dry weight), cooked
    and allowed to cool
4oz (100g) seedless green grapes, halved
2oz (50g) sultanas
2oz (50g) flaked almonds
1oz (25g) chopped walnuts
Lettuce and watercress
1 medium kiwi fruit, sliced

1. In a large bowl, toss the banana slices and apple in the lemon juice.
2. Add the rice, grapes, sultanas, almonds and walnuts and mix well.
3. Line a serving dish with lettuce and watercress, place the banana and nut salad in the centre, and decorate with slices of kiwi fruit.

PASTA AND WALNUT SALAD

Serves: 4
Calories per serving: 190

Beware of eating too many nuts if you want to slim success-fully. It's best to reserve them for salads such as this deli-cious recipe which is ideal for either lunch or supper.

4oz (100g) wholemeal pasta shapes
3 apples
1 tbsp lemon juice
4 sticks celery, sliced thinly
2 tbsp raisins
1oz (25g) stoned dates, chopped
2 tbsp walnuts, chopped
2 tbsp low-fat, natural yogurt
1 tbsp unsweetened orange juice
Salt and black pepper

1. Cook the pasta in plenty of boiling, salted water for about 12 minutes, or until just tender. Rinse under a cold tap and drain thoroughly.
2. Core and thinly slice the apples and toss them in the lemon juice. Stir in the celery, raisins, dates and walnuts.
3. Fold the fruit and nut mixture into the cooked pasta.
4. Mix together the yogurt and orange juice, season to taste and pour over the salad, tossing lightly to blend.

CHAPTER TEN

WICKED DESSERTS

Are you a pudding-shaped person who loves eating puddings? You don't have to give up delicious desserts just because you want to lose weight. On the Fatfield Diet, you can tuck into scrumptious trifles, marvellous meringues, and tasty tarts and still shed pounds, or even stones! But, I do insist that you follow the diet to the letter. That means that you must eat regularly, and enjoy the main course before you have your dessert. This is to ensure that you are not tempted to 'overdose' on that sweet treat.

The recipes below have all been tried out by our Fatfield villagers who vote them tops for taste and easy preparation. Basic ingredients which are useful for slimmers include sugar-free jams, Hermesetas Sprinkle Sweet (which contains one tenth of the calories of sugar), aerosol cream (one 'squirt' of Anchor aerosol cream is about 10 calories, compared with 55 calories for 1 level tablespoon of double cream), Shape Single (15 calories per 1 level tablespoon), and meringue nests which are just 55 calories each and can be topped with fresh or canned (in juice) fruit to make an instant pud.

Following the Fatfield principle of eating more to weigh less, do make these desserts look even bigger on the plate by adding low-calorie extras. Try slices of melon, grapes, orange slices, or a posh-looking 'coulis', simply a runny fruit purée which is easy to make but looks stunning surrounding a simple pud like slices of mango, peach and pineapple or good old semolina.

LYCHEE AND SHERRY TRIFLE

Serves: 6
Calories per serving: 245

4 trifle sponges
1 tbsp sugar-free jam
4 tbsp sweet sherry
12oz (350g) lychees, fresh or canned in juice
3 egg yolks
2 tsp cornflour
¾pt (425ml) semi-skimmed milk
2 tbsp Hermesetas Sprinkle Sweet
¼pt (150ml) Shape Double
1 kiwi fruit, sliced

1.   Split the trifle sponges and fill with the jam. Place in a glass bowl and dribble over the sherry.
2.   Peel the lychees if using fresh ones or drain canned lychees well and arrange in between and around the sponges.
3.   In a small bowl mix a little milk with the egg yolks and cornflour. Heat the remaining milk until steaming. Pour on to the egg yolks, stirring, and then turn into a small heavy-based, non-stick saucepan.
4.   Cook over a very low heat, stirring all the time, until the custard coats the back of a spoon.
5.   Turn the custard into a basin and stir in the Sprinkle Sweet. Pour the custard over the lychees and sponges and leave until cold.
6.   Whip the Shape Double and pipe or spread on the trifle.
7.   Decorate with slices of kiwi fruit.

RASPBERRY PAVLOVA

Serves: 6
Calories per serving: 265

This is a treat from down under, that will help you slim your down under, too! It consists of a basic meringue base, topped with Shape Double and fresh or frozen raspberries. You can, of course, use other fruit such as strawberries or mandarin oranges.

3 egg whites
6oz (175g) caster sugar
1 tsp cornflour
½ tsp vanilla essence
½ tsp white vinegar
½pt (275ml) Shape Double
8oz (225g) fresh or frozen raspberries

1.   Preheat the oven to 300°F, 150°C, gas mark 2. Draw a 7in (18cm) circle on a piece of non-stick baking paper. Place on a baking sheet.
2.   Whisk the egg whites until very stiff. Mix the sugar with the cornflour and whisk in 1 tablespoon at a time, beating until stiff after each addition. Whisk in the vanilla essence and vinegar.
3.   Spoon or pipe the mixture on to the paper to cover the circle. Reduce the oven to 275°F, 140°C, gas mark 1 and bake for 50–60 minutes or until crisp on top but still soft in the middle. Leave to cool and then peel off the paper.
4.   Whip the Shape Double until it holds its shape. Place the meringue base on a plate and spoon the Double on top.
5.   Decorate with raspberries.

APRICOT AND YOGURT ICECREAM

Serves: 6
Calories per serving: 105

This is so quick to make that you'll wonder why you never thought of making your own icecream before. The saving in calories and fat is considerable. You can adapt the recipe to use with other fruit canned in juice, such as pineapple, mandarin oranges or cherries.

1 large can (15oz/425g) apricots in natural juice
1pt (575ml) natural, whole milk yogurt
Almond essence to taste

1. Drain the apricots, reserving the juice.
2. Liquidize or mash the fruit to a pulp.
3. In a large bowl, mix together the apricot purée and yogurt. Add 3 tablespoons of the apricot juice and almond essence to taste.
4. Turn the mixture into a freezer container. Cover and freeze until almost solid. Then whisk or beat in a food processor to break down the ice crystals.
5. Return the icecream to the freezer and freeze until solid.
6. Remove the icecream from the freezer 30 minutes before serving and place in the fridge to soften slightly.

STRAWBERRY OR MANDARIN CHOCOLATE ROLL

Serves: 8
Calories per serving: 115

This is the best-ever pud for reformed chocoholics. It contains cocoa to give you a lift, but the fromage frais provides protein to help stop you from craving another slice! Strawberries are great for this when available, but it is equally delicious with mandarins, canned in juice.

3 large eggs (size 2), separated
4 tbsp Hermesetas Sprinkle Sweet
1½oz (40g) self-raising flour
1oz (25g) drinking chocolate powder
3 tbsp hot water
4 tbsp low-sugar strawberry jam
8oz (225g) fromage frais
4oz (100g) strawberries or mandarins, canned in juice

1.   Grease and line a 12 × 9in (30 × 23cm) Swiss roll tin with non-stick baking parchment.
2.   Whisk the egg yolks with the Sprinkle Sweet until light and creamy.
3.   Sieve together the flour and the drinking chocolate and fold into the yolk mixture with the hot water.
4.   Whisk the egg whites until stiff but not dry and fold gently into the egg yolks. Turn the mixture into the prepared tin and bake in a hot oven (400°F, 200°C, gas mark 6) for 12–15 minutes or until the sponge springs back when lightly pressed.
5.   Turn out onto a large sheet of greaseproof paper. Quickly trim off the edges and peel off the lining paper. Then roll up with the greaseproof paper inside. Leave to cool.

6. Unroll the sponge gently and spread with the jam, then the fromage frais.

7. Reserve some of the fruit for decoration, and slice the rest. Place the sliced fruit on top of the fromage frais.

8. Re-roll the sponge and place carefully on a serving dish.

9. Decorate with the reserved fruit and a little Sprinkle Sweet.

TONI'S LOW-CALORIE SEMOLINA

Serves: 2–3
Calories per serving: For 2, 90; for 3, 60

Fatfield slimming counsellor, Toni Tompsett, whizzes up this basic semolina to feed her family – and herself. She adds a teaspoon of low-calorie jam (adds 10 calories), a pinch of ground nutmeg, or fruit. Occasionally, she mixes it with natural, low-fat yogurt.

½pt (275ml) skimmed milk
2 tbsp semolina
Hermesetas Sprinkle Sweet to taste

1. Heat the milk in a small pan nearly to boiling point.

2. Stir in the semolina, and cook gently for 2 minutes, stirring all the time.

3. Remove from the heat and stir in the sweetener before serving.

COLD RHUBARB CRUMBLE

Serves: 4
Calories per serving: 90

Everyone has a favourite crumble recipe, but for slimmers the main problem is that most crumbles need butter in the topping. This one is different because the topping is simply crushed digestive biscuits. The rhubarb is absolutely delicious mixed with a carton of low-fat rhubarb yogurt. Use the same recipe with apple purée mixed with low-fat blackcurrant yogurt, or raspberries with raspberry or mandarin low-fat yogurt.

1lb (450g) rhubarb, chopped
Grated rind and juice of 1 orange
A little Hermesetas Sprinkle Sweet to taste
1 carton (4½oz/125g) low-fat rhubarb yogurt
4 medium digestive biscuits, crushed
½ tsp mixed spice
Orange slices to decorate

1.   Put the rhubarb, orange rind and juice in a large pan. Stew until soft, then leave to cool.
2.   Blend the mixture in a blender or pass through a sieve to make a purée. Add the sweetener to taste.
3.   Stir in the yogurt, and pour into 1 large, or 4 individual glass bowls.
4.   Mix the biscuits with the mixed spice and spoon over the fruit. Chill.
5.   Decorate with orange slices, and serve.

LINDISFARNE CREAM

Serves: 6
Calories per serving: 140

This is a traditional Geordie dish, using the wonderful mead which comes from the island of Lindisfarne. In this recipe, it is made the low-calorie way. If you don't like mead, you can use sweet sherry instead. Children may prefer it made with apple or orange juice.

1lb (450g) cooking apples, peeled, cored and sliced
3 eggs, separated
2 tbsp Hermesetas Sprinkle Sweet
2 tsp powdered gelatine
3 tbsp water
1 tbsp lemon juice
1 tbsp mead, preferably from Lindisfarne
¼pt (150ml) Shape Double to decorate

1. Cook the apples in a little water until soft. Mash well or purée and allow to cool.
2. In a large bowl whisk together the egg yolks and Sprinkle Sweet until pale and creamy.
3. Fold in the apple purée.
4. Prepare the gelatine by sprinkling it onto 3 tablespoons of cold water in a cup. Leave to stand for 5 minutes. Place the cup in a pan containing a little simmering water and leave until the gelatine is dissolved. Or microwave on Defrost for 30 seconds. Stir the dissolved gelatine into the apple mixture, together with the lemon juice and mead.
5. Beat the egg whites until stiff and fold into the mixture.
6. Pour into a glass dish, and chill until set.
7. Decorate with whipped Shape Double.

SLIMMERS' APPLE BREAD PUDDING

Serves: 4
Calories per serving: 215

This pud is full of fibre, and so filling that you probably won't be able to get up from the table without groaning. Children will love this, served hot for supper, with a scoop of home-made icecream on top.

4 large slices wholemeal bread
1oz (25g) sultanas
¾pt (425ml) semi-skimmed milk
2 eggs
Vanilla essence to taste
3 apples, cored and thinly sliced
¼ tsp ground nutmeg
¼ tsp ground cinnamon

1. Cut the bread slices into quarters and line a shallow ovenproof dish. Sprinkle with the sultanas.
2. Lightly beat the milk and eggs in a bowl, add a few drops of vanilla essence, and strain over the bread. Leave to stand for 30 minutes.
3. Top with the apple slices, and sprinkle with nutmeg and cinnamon.
4. Bake for 30–40 minutes in a moderate oven (350°F, 180°C, gas mark 4) until set. Flash under a hot grill to make the apples go golden brown.

CHOCOLATE MOUSSE

Serves: 4
Calories per serving: 45

Everyone's favourite pud, but strictly out of bounds for slimmers? Not if you make it this way, discovered by Toni!

1 carton (7.7oz/215g) Carnation Light unsweetened
    condensed semi-skimmed milk
2 tsp powdered gelatine
4 tbsp water
1 sachet Ovaltine Options Choc-Orange or Choc-o-Lait
    drink
Mandarin segments to decorate

1.   Chill the carton of Carnation Light overnight in the fridge.
2.   Sprinkle the gelatine onto 2 tablespoons of cold water in a cup. Leave to soak for 5 minutes. Stand the cup in a pan containing a little simmering water and leave until the gelatine is dissolved. Or microwave on Defrost for 30 seconds.
3.   Mix the Ovaltine Options with 2 tablespoons hot water to a smooth paste.
4.   Whip the Carnation Light until very frothy. Continue whipping and adding the dissolved gelatine and chocolate mixture.
5.   Turn into a serving dish or 4 individual dishes and chill until set. Decorate with mandarin segments.

SIX QUICK AND EASY PUDS

Serves: 1

1.   Bake 1 large banana with the juice of ½ orange and a pinch of cinnamon. *Calories: 125*.

2.   Place one ½ 5oz (150g) pot of Ambrosia Light Rice on a dish, top with ½ a peach, canned in juice. Sprinkle with cinnamon and flash under the grill. *Calories: 130*.

3.   Place 1 small ready-made meringue nest on a plate, top with a few green grapes and 1 tablespoon low-fat fromage frais. *Calories: 90*.

4.   Make a crunchy 'sundae' with layers of low fat fruit yogurt, chopped fresh fruit and bran flakes. Calories using 1 carton (4½oz/125g) Diet Ski yogurt, 1 pear, ½oz (15g) Bran Flakes: *150*.

5.   Put 2oz (50g) blackberries in a dish, slosh on 1 tablespoon cassis liqueur and top with 1 tablespoon natural, low-fat yogurt. *Calories: 70*.

6.   Make your own mini 'cheesecake' by crumbling 1 digestive biscuit in a dish and adding 1 tablespoon low-fat soft cheese and a squeeze of lemon juice. *Calories: 100*, or, double everything up for just *200* calories!

FATFIELD FAVOURITES

Here's a list of branded foods and drinks which our Fatfield slimmers found especially helpful and delicious on the diet:

FOOD	SIZE	CALORIES
Breakfast Cereals		
Kellogg's Sultana Bran	1oz (25g)	91
Quaker Puffed Wheat	1oz (25g)	93
Shredded Wheat	1	80
Weetabix	1	65
Cereal Bars		
Quaker Harvest Crunch Chocolate and Raisin	1	80
Crispbreads		
Ryvita Original	1 slice	25
RyKing Brown	1 slice	35
Dairy Products		
St Ivel Shape Soft Cheese with Garlic and Herbs	150g pot	220
Shape Full Flavoured Cheddar Type	1oz (25g)	73
Shape Fromage Frais	100g pot	
Apricot or orange flavour		60
Strawberry or raspberry flavour		65
Shape French Style Set Yogurts	125g pot	50
St Ivel Gold	1oz (25g)	110
Diet Ski Yogurts	125g pot	50
Delight Half Fat Cheddar cheese	1oz (25g)	80

Delight Half Fat Cheese Spread Portions	1	35
Low Fat Dairy Spread with Medium Fat Cheese	1oz (25g)	52
Low Fat Soft Cheese with Garlic and Herbs	1oz (25g)	42
Delight Extra Low	1oz (25g)	56

Drinks

Ovaltine Options, all flavours	1 cup	40
Boots Shapers Apple and Blackberry drink (undiluted)	1fl oz (28ml)	2
McEwans LA low-alcohol beer	440ml can	65
John Smith's low alcohol bitter	½pt/275ml bottle	45
Eisberg Alcohol Free Wine	1 glass	35

Puddings

Bird's Sugar Free Jelly	1 pack	45
Ambrosia Devon Custard	150g pot	150
Ross Mousse, all flavours	1 tub	90

Ready Meals

Findus Lean Cuisine:

Chili Con Carne	1 pack	275
Kashmiri Chicken Curry	1 pack	275
Cod Mornay	1 pack	180
Spaghetti Bolognaise	1 pack	240
Lamb Tikka Masala	1 pack	260
Chicken à l'Orange with Almond Rice	1 pack	270
Beef and Pork Cannelloni with Mornay Sauce	1 pack	235

Batchelors Slim a Meals:

Chicken Risotto, Beef Risotto, Chow Mein, Paella	1 pack	250

Snacks

Golden Wonder Pot Noodles:

Beef and Tomato	1 pot	315
Chicken and Mushroom	1 pot	330
Chow Mein	1 pot	325
Spicy Beef Curry	1 pot	340

Soups

Batchelors Slim a Soups, all flavours	1 sachet	40
Batchelors Slim a Soup Specials, all flavours	1 sachet	60
Heinz Weight Watchers Soups	10.4oz/295g can	
Celery	1 can	60
Chicken	1 can	65
Chicken Noodle or Minestrone	1 can	55

Spreads

Delight Ardennes or Brussels Pâté	1oz (25g)	61
Shippams Salmon or Sardine and Tomato Paste	1.23oz (35g) pot	50

Sweeteners

Hermesetas Sprinkle Sweet	1 tsp	2

INDEX OF RECIPES

150

INDEX